To
BRIGADIER GENERAL BONNER FELLERS
and
DR. KENNETH COLGROVE
I dedicate this volume
in grateful remembrance
of kind words

It gives me great pleasure to see RE-ECHO published some fifty years after my father's death. I am grateful for the encouragement of my good friend, General Bonner Fellers, and for the kind advice of Professor Kenneth Colgrove of Northwestern University. And I thank dear Miss Nancy Jane Fellers for her endeavor.

KAZUO HEARN KOIZUMI

TOKYO, JAPAN

Editor's Preface

The fate of our civilization may depend upon our understanding of the Far East. Already, in the West, we are feeling the impact from our ever-increasing awareness of the vast and complex Orient.

With ponderous China under Communist domination, Japan, Formosa, and the Philippines rise out of the Pacific as steppingstones back to Asia. In the face of encroachment by the monstrous Red spectre, the importance of our Far Eastern friends increases.

Half a century ago, there lived a writer, Lafcadio Hearn, who, lured by the power of the East, wrote about a people as different from us as if they had been from another planet. He gave us a profound insight into their lives.

Lafcadio Hearn probed deeply into the mystery and meaning of life. A restless wanderer, the years swept him from Europe to America and finally to Japan. Wherever he went, the spirit of human life fascinated him.

Lafcadio Hearn did not go as a missionary to Japan. In fact, he thought he hated missionaries. But, without realizing it, he was to become possibly the greatest missionary ever to interpret the West to the Japanese. Through him the Japanese were given a true understanding of the Christian peoples.

It has been said by some of Lafcadio's former students that, so far as is known, none of his Japanese students was in sympathy with Japan's war against the United States.

A prodigious worker, Hearn mastered the art of writing. He strove always for the perfection of simplicity. He never rested until his words achieved their exact meaning. Even after illness attacked his frail frame, his vigorous work continued. He wrote assiduously until the day of his death, September 26, 1904.

During the half century following Lafcadio Hearn's death, time, the most severe and exacting of critics, has been able to judge his work.

Lafcadio Hearn's writing will live.

In view of our need to know about the Orient and Hearn's genius for interpretation, one may safely predict that, before long, most of his books will be republished. In his work lurks the wonder, courage, and wisdom which adventure demands of those who seek to discover.

Soon after his arrival in Japan, Lafcadio Hearn married a Japanese named Setsuko Koizumi. Kazuo Hearn Koizumi, the author of RE-ECHO, is their son. RE-ECHO contains Lafcadio Hearn's last unpublished source material and original sketches.

Lafcadio Hearn was born on the island of Leucadia, June 27, 1850. Leucadia, famed in mythology as the exotic land of the Lotus Eaters, is a rocky island off the coast of Greece.

Lafcadio's mother, Rosa Cassimati,[1] was Greek and very beautiful; hers was a noble family of Kythera (or Cythera) in the Ionian Islands.

His father, Charles Bush Hearn, a doctor in the English army, was mostly Irish and quite gay. Hearn was a descendent of Sir Hugh de Heron, king of gypsies, a well-known North Country baronet mentioned in Sir Walter Scott's *Marmion.* Sir Hugh owned Ford Castle in Northumberland. The crest of his banner was "The Heron Seeks the Heights!" Lafcadio was to adopt the heron as his emblem.

Hearn is a gypsy name, common to several languages, meaning "to roam, stray, become outlawed." And the word Leucadia also signifies "to wander." These meanings were to have a prophetic significance in the life of the eternal wanderer, Lafcadio Hearn.

When Lafcadio was thirty-three, he wrote of his wanderlust:

. . . I would give anything to be a literary Columbus,—to discover a Romantic America in some West Indian or North African or Oriental region. . . . If I could only become a Consul at Bagdad, Algiers, Ispahan, Benares, Samarkand, Nippo, Bangkok, Ninh-Binh,—or any part of the world where ordinary Christians do not like to go! . . .[2]

Lafcadio's whole energy was directed toward a passionate desire to be a "literary Columbus." His writings are as unusual and musical and mysterious as the names of the strange, faraway places he constantly longed to visit.

When Lafcadio was a small child, his father took him and his mother to England. Army duty kept him away from home much of the time.

---

[1] Kazuo Hearn Koizumi, letter to Nancy Jane Fellers (unpublished), August 4, 1953.

[2] Elizabeth Bisland, *The Life and Letters of Lafcadio Hearn* (2 vols.; Boston: Houghton Mifflin Company, 1906), I, 294-95.

And, somehow, something sad happened, for Lafcadio's mother and father found they were not suited to each other. It was decided that Lafcadio would remain in Dublin to grow up with the Hearn family. His father was ordered to India, and Lafcadio never saw him again.

Lafcadio's mother returned to Greece, and Lafcadio was never to see her again. Yet the vision of a beautiful mother clung to him always. Perhaps it was a childhood memory of happy days with her that years later moved him to write:

I have a memory of a place and a magical time, in which the sun and the moon were larger and brighter than now. . . . I know the sky was very much more blue, and nearer to the world. . . . The sea was alive, and used to talk—and the Wind made me cry out for joy when it touched me. . . . Also in that place the clouds were wonderful and of colours . . . that used to make me hungry and thirsty. . . . And all that country and time were softly ruled by One who thought only of ways to make me happy. . . . When day was done, and there fell the great hush of the night before moonrise, she would tell me stories that made me tingle from head to foot with pleasure. . . . At last there came a parting day; and she wept and told me of a charm she had given that I must never, never lose, because it would keep me young, and give me power to return. But I never returned. And the years went; and one day I knew that I had lost the charm, and had become ridiculously old.[3]

_____
[3] *Ibid.*, I, 4-5.

At the age of sixteen Lafcadio was blessed with a youthful exuberance that kept him oblivious of the fact that he was short and not physically impressive. But, while he was playing the game Giant's Stride, a tragic event occurred. A wooden handle on the knotted end of a rope struck him in the left eye and totally blinded it.

Until this time Lafcadio had enjoyed a measure of self-confidence. However, losing the sight of one eye did more than change his appearance. It marked his entire life. His blind eye appeared altogether dead. In the other eye he was so nearsighted that he could not see clearly beyond six inches, even with lenses. As Lafcadio developed into an insatiable reader, his nearsighted eye became greatly enlarged. More and more he grew shy and self-conscious because he thought himself grotesquely ugly. But many of his friends said that, actually, he had handsome features and a fine profile. His sensitive nature subjected him to many inner hurts and bruises.

Lafcadio was nineteen when he came to the United States. He wandered from city to city, writing for American newspapers: the *Cincinnati Enquirer*, *New Orleans Item*, *New Orleans Times-Democrat* and *New York Tribune*. Some of the magazines that published his work were: the *Atlantic Monthly, Cosmopolitan, Harper's Weekly, Harper's Monthly* and *Harper's Bazaar.*

Nevertheless, one would be mistaken to believe that Lafcadio's life in the United States became one of ease. He had a wretched struggle, financially and socially. Just imagine a man more shy than the shyest child cracking the newspaper business! One editor remembers Lafcadio entering his office, plunking a manuscript down on the desk, and disappearing from the room like a frightened deer.

Shyness made it impossible for Lafcadio to be an aggressive newspaper reporter. Once he returned without a story because he was too shy to seek entrance to the home of the man he was assigned to interview. It looked as if Lafcadio expected the man to come out and say, "Won't you please come on in and interview me?"

Lafcadio generally avoided social gatherings. He felt himself inadequate in society. But, because he lived within himself, he had more time for study and introspection. Ceaseless application became the mother of his art.

Often Lafcadio was hungry and miserable. He wisely wrote: "It is regret and desire and the Spirit of Unrest that provoketh poetry and romance."[4]

Lafcadio tells the story of a pet grasshopper who, not being fed, ate his own legs. Lafcadio says (and how well he knew) —

> Yet, after all, to devour one's own legs for hunger is not the worst that can happen to a being cursed with the gift of song. There are human crickets who must eat their own hearts in order to sing.[5]

In Cincinnati his "first small job" had been to sell little handmade mirrors. When he put his tray down on the curb, one of the mirrors was broken. The man who had hired him exploded in a rage and made a scene to which the passersby crowded. Lafcadio ran home without even collecting his salary. Because he could not pay his rent, he was put out of his room. All possessions, even a cherished picture of his father, were seized. This was just one of the many misfortunes that befell him.

Yet, in spite of the troubles that ringed him round, Lafcadio was never tempted to turn to the philosophy that seeks to snare the unfortunate and dissatisfied. For, politically, Lafcadio had uncanny insight.

---

[4] *Ibid.*, I, 194.

[5] Lafcadio Hearn, *Kottō* (New York: The Macmillan Company, 1902), p. 241.

In 1878 he wrote an editorial titled: "Were There Communists in Antiquity?"

The efforts of communism had only a temporary success, and their ultimate result was the establishment of a despotism at once merciless and all-powerful. A violent outbreak of communism in this republic might lead to a change in government which would leave the riotous class everything to regret.[6]

And, in 1904, he wrote:

But I fear that I must shock you by my declaration of non-sympathy with much of the work of contemporary would-be reformers. They are toiling for socialism; and socialism will come. It will come very quietly and gently, and tighten about nations as lightly as a spider's web; and then there will be revolutions! Not sympathy and fraternity and justice—but a Terror in which no man will dare to lift his voice.

. . . The rule of the many will be about as merciful as a calculating-machine, and as moral as a lawn-mower. What socialism means really no one seems to know or care. It will mean the most insufferable oppression that ever weighed upon mankind.[7]

To understand Lafcadio's spiritual struggles it is necessary to look at his first disillusioning encounter with formal theology. A grimly religious friend of Lafcadio's aunt had not learned that true Christians should be joyful and understanding. She threatened that God would punish him because he was afraid of goblins. She screamed this idea at him in such a terrifying manner that, to Lafcadio, God was not kind but vengeful and capricious and One to be greatly feared.

Lafcadio was unusually imaginative. As some children do, he dreamed about all sorts of weird creatures and goblins which frightened him. There were times, in nightmares, when he felt the awful terror of a shadow monster hovering over his bed. And, in the dream, Lafcadio would be unable to cry out or make any move to save himself.

Instead of calming his fears, his elders surmised that he was wicked and that the goblin world of his vivid imagination was the work of the devil himself. He was put to bed in the dark for punishment and told that there were no such things as goblins. This was hard for Lafcadio to reconcile because he was certain that he had really seen them in his dreams. He was just a little boy with a stupendous imagination. A light in his room, a kind word, would have helped him to understand earlier the difference between dreams and reality. Instead, he was goaded with threats of hell.

Subsequently all attempts to indoctrinate him in a formal religion failed. His antipathy toward missionaries was probably augmented

[6] Lafcadio Hearn, "Were There Communists in Antiquity?" editorial, *New Orleans Item*, August 23, 1878.

[7] Bisland, *op. cit.*, II, 511-12.

by his early tangle with dogma. Yet, throughout his life, Lafcadio was to live as many Christians never dare. He was a man imbued in the awful and wonderful awareness of a great, unseen Spiritual Power. He was kind to the weak and defenseless. Exploitation and cruelty were impossible for him.

Before he came to the United States, Lafcadio was sent to school in England and in France. Under the Jesuits in France he learned to read and write the precisely exquisite French language. He was such an excellent student that, later, he was able to translate into English hundreds of French manuscripts.

Ordinarily translations lose much of their original beauty. Lafcadio's translations not only retain their inner charm but, oftentimes, are an actual improvement on the original work of the author! Lafcadio translated such talented French stylists as Gautier, de Maupassant, Flaubert, Coppée, Daudet, and Zola. This work sharpened his own future writing.

As a book reviewer, Lafcadio was brilliant. Dr. Rudolph Matas, one of Lafcadio's closest friends, said:

Hearn's capacity for reading swiftly and for getting to the heart of a book was amazing when his ocular handicaps are considered. While others read sentences, he read paragraphs, chapters. . . . Swiftly as he read, it would be found on questioning him afterward that nothing worth while had been overlooked, and he could refer back and find any passage unvaryingly. I had occasion to test this on several occasions when he would receive books for review, and often that was put off until the night before it was due. I would look the next day, and to my astonishment would see the review in perfect form, impeccable in every way, and yet it seems incredible that such perfect and complex work could be done with that one crippled eye. . . .[8]

Lafcadio Hearn believed fervently that:

. . . No man is really able to read a book who is not able to express an original opinion regarding the contents of a book.

He considered reading a science:

. . . For, after all, the good book of fiction or romance or poetry is a scientific work; it has been composed according to the best principles . . . of the great science of life, the knowledge of human nature.[9]

Lafcadio Hearn was a vessel in which the scientific and the artistic met. Many hours he and his friend Dr. Rudolph Matas would talk about the science of the human body and the effect of fever upon it. Then Lafcadio incorporated his scientific knowledge into his art.

[8] Dr. Rudolph Matas, "Some Reminiscences of Hearn in New Orleans," in *Lafcadio Hearn in New Orleans* (New Orleans: The Lafcadio Hearn Society; New York: Japan Institute, Inc., March 7, 1941), p. 15.

[9] Lafcadio Hearn, *Talks to Writers*; ed. by John Erskine (New York: Dodd, Mead and Company, 1920), pp. 187-88.

Never satisfied with imperfection, Lafcadio went over his work many times. His habits for journalism and literature were completely different. He made a distinction between them: ". . . journalism cannot wait, and the best literature must wait."* Nevertheless, his journalistic writings had an artistic quality which set them apart from the mundane.

Lafcadio b e l i e v e d that, when words are in print, their faults of arrangement are more e v i d e n t. Therefore he was especially intense about correcting his copy when the publishers sent it to him in galley-proof form. He was extremely particular about punctuation. Often he used both a comma and a dash, or a dash and a semicolon. In fact, he acquired the nickname "Old Semicolon."

Lafcadio Hearn believed that the genius of the English language lies in the fact that the more accurately the writer is able to express his feeling, the shorter and the less involved and the clearer the work becomes. His writing is direct and powerful. With haunting clarity, he captivates by the genius of his expression. A dynamic force proceeds from the man who was as mysterious as Poe's "The Raven." For Lafcadio Hearn creates an atmosphere similar to the mood created by "nevermore," in "The Raven." This mood was described by a friend who, hearing Lafcadio cough in the night, went to aid him:

. . . Not wanting, however, to disturb him, if he was at work, I cautiously opened the door just a little, and peeped in. I saw my friend intent in writing at his high desk, with his nose almost touching the paper. Leaf after leaf he wrote on. In a while he held up his head, and what did I see! It was not the Hearn I was familiar with; it was another Hearn. His face was mysteriously white; his large eye gleamed. He appeared like one in touch with some unearthly presence.[10]

The word "mystic" comes nearest to describing the inner comprehension of Lafcadio Hearn. He once said:

It may be that profundities of self,— abysses never reached by any ray from the life of sun,—are strangely stirred in slumber, . . .[11]

There was one dream Lafcadio had over and over, and he wrote it down. In the dream he would be reading a big book:

I do not know the name of the book, nor the name of its author: I have not been able to see the title page; and there is no running title. As for the back of the volume, it remains,—like the back of the Moon,—invisible forever.
At no time have I touched the book in

---

* Matas, *op. cit.*, p. 31.

[10] Nobushige Amenomori, "Lafcadio Hearn, the Man," *Atlantic Monthly*, XCVI (October, 1905), 524.

[11] Lafcadio Hearn, *Shadowings* (Boston: Little, Brown and Company, 1910), p. 246.

any way,—not even to turn a leaf. Somebody, always viewless, holds it up and open before me in the dark; and I can read it only because it is lighted by a light that comes from nowhere. Above and beneath and on either side of the book there is darkness absolute; but the pages seem to retain the yellow glow of lamps that once illuminated them.

A queer fact is that I never see the entire text of a page at once, though I see the whole page itself plainly. The text rises, or seems to rise, to the surface of the paper as I gaze, and fades out almost immediately after having been read.[12]

The following is a fragment from a dream which Lafcadio remembered long enough to write down.

Then the Wave prayed to remain a wave forever.
The Sea made answer:—
Nay, thou must break; there is no rest in me.[13]

In a d d i t i o n to this beautiful, mystic revelation, prophetic eeriness springs from Lafcadio's works. For example, he wrote a story called "Chita" and dedicated it to Dr. Matas. It was in this story that Lafcadio describes fever by using the scientific information he had obtained from the doctor. The story was about a little girl who survived the total annihilation of a summer-resort island by a tropical storm.

Twenty years after *Chita* was published, events like those of the story came to pass. Grand Isle and Les Chenières were obliterated by a storm which fitted Hearn's description. Even more remarkable was the fact that fishermen rescued a little girl who was later found by her father in much the same manner as in the story which Lafcadio had written.

And again his amazing prophetic wisdom reveals itself in a letter to a friend:

It now seems to me that time is the most precious of all things conceivable. I can't waste it by going out to hear people talk nonsense. . . . There are rich natures that can afford the waste; but I can't, because the best part of my life has been wasted in wrong directions and I shall have to work like thunder till I die to make up for it. . . .[14]

As a modest genius, Lafcadio Hearn may have thought that part of his life had been wasted. But he left to the world volumes of priceless, enchanting prose.

A young West Point graduate, Lieutenant Oscar T. Crosby of the United States Army Corps of Engineers, introduced Lafcadio Hearn to Herbert Spencer's *First Principles*. Spencer made a profound effect on Lafcadio's life by broadening his insight and causing him to think much more deeply. After thorough study of Spencer, Lafcadio wrote:

12 *Ibid.*, pp. 249-50.
13 *Ibid.*, p. 251.
14 Bisland, *op. cit.*, II, 194.

I suddenly discovered what a waste of time all my Oriental metaphysics had been. I also discovered, for the first time, how to apply the little general knowledge I possessed. I also found unspeakable comfort in the sudden, and for me, eternal reopening of the Great Doubt, which renders pessimism ridiculous, and teaches a new reverence for all forms of faith![15]

The "Great Doubt" to Lafcadio meant the mystery that no man has yet been able to solve, the mystery of origin, the mystery of destiny, the mystery of life. Always asking ultimate questions, Lafcadio tussled with the unknown.

It is fortunate that Lafcadio never narrowed himself to any "ism" or "creed." Had he settled for an answer, he might have stopped searching and reaching into the Infinite Unknown. Then his writing would have lost the driving force that makes it great.

Hating the cold of winter in American cities, Lafcadio's gypsy blood had constantly impelled him to drift south. In 1880 he had landed in the French West Indies where the beauty of the tropics captivated him and became a part of his very being. His color descriptions there were especially sensuous: "The sky does not deepen its hue to-day: it brightens it;—the blue glows as if it were taking fire throughout."[16]

Lafcadio's extreme nearsightedness caused his color perception to be unusually sensitive. Dr. Matas said:

. . . While he was the greatest miope among litterateurs, he was, on the other hand, the greatest possessor of a color sense that has existed. It was incredible. . . . He could distinguish color which he associated with form, and he gained form by color.[17]

The colors Lafcadio saw were not bounded by precise lines. His myopia probably magnified any object he looked upon, thereby accentuating the color area. Color dominated his sense impressions, as is evident in many of the drawings in RE-ECHO.

Always intrigued with the wild, exotic, and intense, Lafcadio wrote many other essays on the effects of color. One in particular, about a sunset, dwells upon the color red and the pagan feeling of fear that red provokes:

The most stupendous apparition of red that I ever saw was a tropical sunset in a cloudless sky. . . . It began with a flaming of orange from horizon to zenith; and this quickly deepened into a fervid vermillion, through which the crimson disk glared like the cinder of a burnt-out star. Sea, peak, and palm caught the infernal glow; and I became conscious of a vague strange horror

---

[15] *Ibid.*, I, 86.

[16] Lafcadio Hearn, *Two Years in the French West Indies* (New York: Harper & Brothers, 1890), p. 17.

[17] Matas, *op. cit.*, p. 16.

within myself,—a sense of distress like that which precedes a nightmare. I could not then explain the feeling;—I only knew that the color had aroused it.[18]

All through the primary spectrum he roamed:

Yellow, the color of gold, is also the color of our sun . . . Next to Red, the most emotional color is Yellow—the color of life, and of what men seem to prize next to life —Gold. . . . Red is the color of blood—a color allied necessarily from time immemorial with violent mental impressions, whether of war, or love, or the chase, or religious sacrafice. Green itself is the color of the world . . . the hue associated with all the labors of man on the earth, since he began to labor. It is the color of Industry. . . . Blue—the blue of the far away sky—has necessarily always been for man the color most mysterious and holy—always associated with those high phenomena of heaven which first inspired wonder and fear of the Unknown.[19]

Others of his senses were sharpened by his lack of keen vision— the senses of odor and touch. He associated youth with a special "Parfum de Jeunesse."

He said of touch:

I remember the touch of many hands,— the quality of each clasp, the sense of physical sympathy or repulsion aroused. Thousands I have indeed forgotten,—probably because their contact told me nothing in particular; but the strong experiences I fully recollect.[20]

In order to see detail, Lafcadio would be compelled to put his eye next to the object he was examining. Sometimes he used a magnifying glass. But he had an aversion to eyeglasses. Such close study accounts for many of the tiny details in the RE-ECHO collection.

When he was in the French West Indies, he had written a series of articles for *Harper's Magazine*. Also, *Two Years in the French West Indies* had come out of that sojourn. More and more his skill and force as a writer had become apparent.

But in the West Indies he had fallen sick with a tropical fever, an ordeal which took much of his strength. He returned to the United States, but he did not stay long. Large, modern cities held for him a terror. He wrote to a friend about New York:

. . . Nobody can find anybody, nothing seems to be anywhere, everything seems to be mathematics and geometry and enigmatics and riddles and confusion worse confounded: architecture and mechanics run mad. One has to live by intuition and move by steam. . . . You are improving yourselves out of the natural world. . . . I came in by one door as you went out at the other. Now there are cubic miles of cut granite and iron fury between us. . . .[21]

He had treated London with more sympathy:

---

[18] Lafcadio Hearn, *Exotics and Retrospectives* (Boston: Little, Brown and Company, 1910), p. 251.
[19] Lafcadio Hearn, "Colors and Emotions," *New Orleans Times-Democrat*, May 8, 1887.
[20] Hearn, *Exotics and Retrospectives*, p. 264.

[21] Bisland, *op. cit.*, I, 444.

You will hear the Roar of London growing lower and more distant, till it sinks into a deep, steady hum that lives through the night and deepens into the dawn. Then when the stars come out, if you wander to the Embankment through a million of lights, you may behold a spectacle unapproached in sublimity by any other city of the earth —the black river moaning between its banks of stone; the great masses of Westminster spires looming up in the night; the bridges spanning the stream with their arches of illuminations; the phosperic face of the great clock two hundred feet above you; the granite visage of grim river gods frowning from the corbels of the steamboat piers; and at intervals, the flame-eyed engines roaring by, like monsters, dragging after them their long vertebrae of cars. Then, perhaps you can feel what London is.[22]

Lafcadio was happy to accept when the Canadian Pacific Railroad Company and Steamship Line offered to send him to Japan. His assignment was to write sketches to interest travel to the Orient.

Lafcadio looked upon Japan—enchanted. Here his wanderlust was more nearly satisfied than anywhere else on e a r t h . At last Lafcadio Hearn, the wanderer, had found the place where he seemed to belong. Mysterious Japan fascinated him. When he first saw this magical land, he expressed the desire that, when the time came for him to die it would be among these strange and charming people. He says of his first day in the Orient:

. . . The first charm of Japan is intangible and volatile as a perfume.

I turn a moment to look back through the glorious light. Sea and sky mingle in the same beautiful pale clear blue. Below me the billowing of bluish roofs reaches to the verge of the unruffled bay on the right, and to the feet of the green wooded hills flanking the city on two sides. Beyond that semicircle of green hills rises a lofty range of serrated mountains, indigo silhouettes. And enormously high above the line of them towers an apparition indescribably lovely, —one solitary snowy cone, so filmily exquisite, so spiritually white, that but for its immemorially familiar outline, one would surely deem it a shape of cloud. Invisible its base remains, being the same delicious tint as the sky: only above the eternal snowline its dreamy cone appears, seeming to hang, the ghost of a peak, between the luminous land and the luminous heaven,—the sacred and matchless mountain, Fujiyama.[23]

In Japan he taught English literature in order to earn his living. He was a professor in the cities of Matsue and Kumamoto. He also taught in the Imperial University and Waseda University of Tokyo. He inspired his students to write. And, from them, he learned about the inner thoughts of the Japanese people.

Another of his sources for understanding Japan was his wife. Using the special "mutual Japanese" language they had concocted to communicate, she told him goblin folk

---

[22] Lafcadio Hearn, "London," *New Orleans Item*, June 29, 1878.

[23] Lafcadio Hearn, *Glimpses of Unfamiliar Japan* (Tokyo: Daito Shobo, February 25, 1931), pp. 1, 12-13.

tales and mysteries of his adopted land and people.

Since English was difficult for his Japanese students, Lafcadio was careful to explain every lesson in detail. He spoke slowly and without notes. His lectures were so clear and and interesting that his students took them down in their notebooks, word for word. Later, these lectures were collected with loyal care by his Japanese students. They were published posthumously by Hokuseido Press, Tokyo, Japan, as a *History of English Literature*. This work is among the best interpretations of English literature available today.

The student who knew him best was his son, Kazuo Hearn Koizumi. The name Kazuo signifies "the first of the excellent, best of the peerless."

Lafcadio had found real happiness in Japan. His wife was a lovely and gentle Japanese woman. He had chosen her from among others who would have married him because, although she was poor, she was of fine and noble stock.

In Japan, for the first time in his life, Lafcadio was content. He belonged in his Japanese home. There he could write, and "Mama San" would be careful to see that he was not disturbed. His creative power reached its peak. From 1894 to 1904, in yearly succession, he wrote

Glimpses of Unfamiliar Japan, "Out of the East," Kokoro, Gleanings in Buddha-Fields, Exotics and Retrospectives, The Boy Who Drew Cats, The Goblin Spider, In Ghostly Japan, Shadowings, A Japanese Miscellany, Kottō, Kwaidan, climaxed by the incomparable *Japan; an Attempt at Interpretation.*

Lafcadio was a tender and sympathetic husband and a good father. After his son Kazuo was born, Lafcadio wrote to a friend:

. . . When it was all over, I confess I felt very humble and grateful to the Unknowable Power which had treated us so kindly, —and I said a little prayer of thanks, feeling quite sure it was not foolish to do so.[24]

The name Koizumi is Mrs. Hearn's family name. It means "Little Spring." Lafcadio took this name when he married into the Koizumi family. His son Kazuo retained the name Koizumi. Kazuo Hearn Koizumi, the author of RE-ECHO, lives in Tokyo. He is in his early sixties.

Very carefully Kazuo saved his father's original manuscripts and drawings. He knew that they were important to the world; also, he loved his father very much and treasured the things that had belonged to him.

Although it has been over half a century since Lafcadio died, Kazuo's

---

24 Bisland, *op. cit.,* II, 149.

most cherished memories are of the lessons his father gave him. Some of Kazuo's Copybook, and quite a number of the drawings his father made to explain poetry and arithmetic and geography are reproduced in RE-ECHO. Also, in the end, Kazuo reflects on the futility of war. And the genius of Lafcadio himself gleams through the pages.

How do I come to have the precious and important last unpublished Lafcadio Hearn source material? I shall let the author of RE-ECHO, Kazuo Hearn Koizumi, Lafcadio Hearn's son, tell the story. It is a story of a beautiful friendship.

Kazuo's story:

During the war time, I and my family were all anxious about our good friend Bonner Fellers San of the United States Army.

General Bonner Fellers had been my friend since June 4, 1930. When he first visited at my late mother's house he was a handsome young First Lieutenant, and his pretty wife came in company with him. He wrote in our visitors book as follows: "When I tried to teach Browning and George Meredith and Carlyle at West Point I found that Hearn knew what they were thinking and had gone on beyond them. Then Hearn taught me to love Japan. This is the thrill of a lifetime! Thank you Mrs. Hearn."

And his wife wrote also in a very fine handwriting: "I shall always treasure the memory of my delightful visit in this charming house. Thank you, Mrs. Hearn, for your gracious hospitality."

Thus did my father and mother, Bonner and Dorothy Fellers, meet Kazuo Hearn Koizumi, son of the great writer, Lafcadio Hearn. My father kept in touch with shy Kazuo on his various visits to Japan. When Father flew into Japan on August 29, 1945, with General MacArthur, he sought out Kazuo Hearn Koizumi, who describes their meeting:

My old friend, the goodnatured General Fellers appeared in the hall. He rushed across the blue thick carpeted floor at me. He took my hand with his mighty hand, and he asked me quickly, about my health and my wife and my son. I saw something gleaming in his gray blue eyes. At this instance I preached to myself in the indoor of my heart: "We Japanese were defeated in war by the American new scientific weapons but we Japanese are now defeated by American kindness too."

During the Occupation my father saw Kazuo often. One day, they paid tribute at Lafcadio Hearn's grave. Kazuo tells about it:

General Fellers was the first foreign visitor to Hearn's grave at post war. He offered a big basket full of pretty peony flowers before my parents' tombs. It was quite a memorable pleasant day. . . . The atmosphere which flowed out from his, General Fellers', serious and grand but warm and affectionate heart was just as a perfume of the peony flower or the incense smoke in which we were wrapped.

Then, one day, General Fellers came to us to bid farewell. Ah! We felt so reluctant to part. Though between America and Japan there was a big war, between him and me our friendship had not changed. The words "Forget me not" he frequently said to me,

PHOTOGRAPH TAKEN AT THE GRAVE OF LAFCADIO HEARN

Left to right: Mrs. Kazuo Hearn Koizumi, Toki Koizumi, General Bonner Fellers, and Kazuo Hearn Koizumi

". . . I should like, when my time comes, to be laid away in some Buddhist graveyard of the ancient kind—so that my ghostly company should be ancient, caring nothing for the fashions and the changes and the disintegrations of Meiji. That old cemetery behind my garden would be a suitable place. Everything there is beautiful with a beauty of exceeding and startling queerness; each tree and stone has been shaped by some old, old ideal which no longer exists in any living brain; even the shadows are not of this time and sun, but of a world forgotten, that never knew steam or electricity or magnetism or—kerosene oil!"*

LAFCADIO HEARN

* Lafcadio Hearn, *Kwaidan* (London: Jonathan Cape, 30 Bedford Square, 1927).

and it encouraged me so much. "How can we forget you?" always I replied. Now he is not a young officer, and my hairs are growing gray too. After we saw him off we went into our room with a great melancholy. I took up the lighter which he had left for me, lit a fire on my ancestral pipe and murmured with the smoke: "When shall we meet again?" I heard my wife sobbing. Suddenly my boy shouted: "I will meet him at America!"[25]

Such words of friendship for my father reveal the depth, sincerity, and expressive genius in Re-Echo's a u t h o r , Kazuo Hearn Koizumi. Kazuo Hearn Koizumi had shown my father the drawings that appear in Re-Echo. He had told my father about how Lafcadio taught with the drawings and by the Copybook. With enthusiasm my father said, "You must write this. What a wonderful book it would make!" Dr. Kenneth Colgrove, the distinguished professor from Northwestern University, also gave Kazuo sympathetic encouragement. You will see his name in the dedication. And that is how Kazuo Hearn Koizumi came to write Re-Echo.

In searching for a title he remembered his father's story, "Nymph Echo"—written long ago in Kazuo's Copybook.

Once there was a beautiful girl called Echo. She was the daughter of a god. So she ought to have been happy. But she could

not get the husband she wanted; and she became so unhappy that all her body melted into the air, and only her voice remained. She could speak; but she could only repeat other people's words. And she does that still.

If you go to the mountain, and call her, she will repeat what you say.

If you ask:—"Where are you?"—she will answer:—"Where are you?"

If you cry out, "Come here!"—she will repeat, "Come here!" If you shout, "Go away," she will repeat, "Go away!" If you beat a drum, she will beat a ghostly drum. —Do not forget her name.

Echo.

Echo, poor Echo!

Kazuo adds:

"And I remember that my father said frequently with a lost countenance—'My work is only an echo.' One day I replied, 'Echo is my good friend. If there were no Echo, how lonesome the world would be!' To this he smiled and he kissed me on my cheek. And so I call the Hearn sketches, Re-Echo.'

Because children are so near to their source of profundity, a great artist is likely to understand them. Always, with Lafcadio Hearn and his boy Kazuo, there was a beautiful blend of discipline and inspiration. So eager was Lafcadio for Kazuo to learn that he gave the boy an English lesson when he was only eighteen months old! Kazuo was almost six years old when the study of English began in earnest.

25 Kazuo Hearn Koizumi, "A Cordial Friendship" (Unpublished manuscript).

And Lafcadio Hearn, like the greatest ballet or music masters, drilled his son well. Kazuo stood like a soldier to learn pronunciation. It was painful for him to create the strange English sounds, sounds shaped by different muscles from those used in speaking Japanese. Lafcadio was severely strict. He would drill Kazuo until, sometimes, Kazuo would cry. Lafcadio was not insensible to these tears, for he dictated to Kazuo to put in the Copybook:

> On the glass shōji of papa's room, there are little marks like marks made by the trickling of raindrops. These marks are made by the tears of papa's dear little boy. It makes papa very sorry to see them; but every little boy must cry when he begins to learn—and the glass can be washed.

One day, after a long and intense session, Kazuo was unhappy because his father called him back to the study. Kazuo expected more lessons. But, to Kazuo's delight, his father merely wanted to share the beautiful sunset with him.

Lafcadio Hearn loved his son in a way that reaches deep into the mystery of life. He wrote to a friend:

> ... My whole anxiety is now about him. ... ... If anything were to happen to *him*, the sun would go out. ... I must do all I can to feed the tiny light, and give it a chance to prove what it is worth. ... I must not risk the blowing out of the little lamp.[26]

---

[26] Bisland, *op. cit.*, II, 181, 476.

Lafcadio's faith in his son was well justified. In RE-ECHO we see that "the little lamp" is still burning with a bright and beautiful light. If Lafcadio Hearn had lived a few years longer to continue Kazuo's lessons, Kazuo's inherited ability might have grown to equal that of the master himself. For, certainly, the boy was unusual. His grasp of the English language when he was only ten was remarkable.

Lafcadio considered Kazuo as a distinct individual personality, given of God. Into Kazuo's complete inner world Lafcadio poured the same insight and energy that he lavished upon his classic prose. True to his own beliefs was such a practice, for he had written:

> ... Self-cursèd he who denies the divinity of love! Each heart, each brain in the billions of humanity,—even so surely as sorrow lives,—feels and thinks in some special way unlike any other; and goodness in each has its unlikeness to all other goodness,—and thus its own infinite preciousness; for however humble, however small, it is something all alone, and God never repeats his work. No heart-beat is cheap, no gentleness is despicable, no kindness is common; and Death, in removing a life,—the simplest life ignored,—removes what never will reappear through the eternity of eternities,—since every being is the sum of a chain of experiences infinitely varied from all others. ...[27]

RE-ECHO's reason for being is love. Lafcadio Hearn taught his boy

---

[27] Hearn, *Two Years in the French West Indies*, p. 379.

Kazuo the beauty of language and poetry. What Kazuo learned has enriched his life. And it is his hope that both Western and Eastern youngsters and their parents will rediscover such treasure.

In RE-ECHO we enter into an intimate relationship. Father and son learn from each other, and both lives are quickened. And, in RE-ECHO, the world of the East and the world of the West meet in the sensitive soul of a ten-year-old boy. May these worlds meet again.

NANCY JANE FELLERS

SPRINGLAND LANE
WASHINGTON, D.C.

September 26, 1954

Author's Preface

When my father, Lafcadio Hearn, came to Japan in 1890, he stood on the deck of the ship in the earliest dawn. With a delicious shock of surprise he saw the ghostly, dream-white peak of Mount Fuji against the morning blue. Much higher than the range of the island mountains, Fujiyama seemed to hang in the sky like a delicate phantom film. But, with the glow of sunrise, its spotless tip pinkened like the point of some wondrous bud. Then it became gold-white.

And when Father first set foot on Japan, he exclaimed, "I want to die here!" In Japan he would find peace.

But the tide of Occidental civilization rushed against these remote islands and forced a violent trans-figuration. Unavoidably drawn into the vortex, Father's inner turmoil began again. And the traditions and romances of ancient Japan became his lifeboat to carry him across the rough tide.

While he pulled the oars in the surging sea, his clear voice sang of both the East and of the West. And his words echoed rhythmically into many lands.

With great tenacity Father instructed me in this same beauty of expression. But, alas, his death was too quick! Although I am not as gifted as Father, I hope the reader may hear our voices in RE-ECHO as they break through the surging Eastern tides.

KAZUO HEARN KOIZUMI

Table of Contents

List of Illustrations

RE-ECHO

Words from the Great--- Interpretations

My father, Lafcadio Hearn, often drew a picture to explain the poems which he gave me as English lessons. He had a habit of drawing pictures on the margin and reverse side of his writing paper, or on the blotting paper on his writing desk. I take much interest in these pictures for I believe something of his individuality is well expressed in them.

CHRISTOPHER SMART AND ALFRED LORD TENNYSON

One day Father gave me a study to read and explain. It was the poem "Adoration," by Christopher Smart, the last two stanzas of which I quote:

Strong is the lion—like a coal
His eyeball—like a bastion's mole
  His chest against the foes;
Strong the gier-eagle on his sail;
Strong against tide th' enormous whale
  Emerges as he goes:

But stronger still, in earth and air
And in the sea, the man of prayer,
  And far beneath the tide,

And in the seat to faith assigned,
Where ask is have; where seek is find;
  Where knock is open wide.

Fortunately, that day I read well and translated without many mistakes. And Father asked for my impressions. "I want to know much more about the eagle," I replied, "because the verse about the eagle is too brief." Father was amused by my request and began to tell many interesting stories about eagles. While he was talking about the eagles, he seemed to catch some idea. He rushed to one of his bookcases and took out the works of Alfred Lord Tennyson. And he gave me a verse to read.

After my reading was finished, Father praised it enthusiastically. Then he dismissed me from his study. When I left his study, he kissed me and promised that he would paint some pictures about the eagle for me. The next day he gave me this

THE EAGLE

"He clasps the crag with crooked hands;
Close to the sun in lonely lands,
Ring'd with the azure world, he stands.

The wrinkled sea beneath him crawls;
He watches from his mountain walls,
And like a thunderbolt he falls."

ALFRED LORD TENNYSON

. . . O that I were a cloud . . .
to drift forever with the
hollow wind!—O that I
were a wave to pass from
ocean to ocean, and chant my
freedom in foam upon the
rocks of a thousand coasts!—
O that I might live even as the
Eagle, who may look into the face of
the everlasting sun!*

* Lafcadio Hearn, *Fantastics and Other Fancies* (Boston: Houghton Mifflin Company, 1914), p. 180.

picture (see page 37). It was painted on the reverse side of his rough
draft of "Drifting," from *A Japanese Miscellany.*

Father went frequently to the picture exhibitions held at Ueno Park,
Tokyo. He enjoyed buying pictures
without paying any attention to the
painter's name. One day Father ac-
companied Mother and me to the
exhibition. And I found a very interesting picture.

"Papa, there is a picture just like
'The Eagle' which you painted for
me the other day." I took my
father's hand and led him before
the picture.

"Oh, it is fine! How do you like
the picture?" he asked me. Then,
"Do you think it good?" he asked
Mother. And then he bought it.

The picture was painted on silk
with Japanese water colors, a scene
of dark-gray, gigantic, rocky cliffs
standing in arrangement. Colored
in at the back of the heaps are rosy-
ish, faint, purple lights of dawn. I
fail to remember the painter's name,
but I am sure it is someone who belongs to the Okakura's Bijutsuin
school. Father was very fond of it.
He sent it to be mounted as a *kakemono* ("hanging picture") and then
hung it in the *tokonoma* ("alcove").

It was the morning of his last
day, the twenty-sixth of September,
1904, that he said to my mother:

"I had a very unusual dream last night.
I traveled for a long distance . . . not a
journey in Europe, nor in Japan—it was a
strange place." Mother said he seemed to
be enjoying himself.[1]

After my father's death, I heard
from some travelers that the island
where Lafcadio Hearn was born is
a very rocky place, and it is famous
for the Leucadian Rock or "Sappho's
Leap," because there is a legend that
the poetess of antiquity, Sappho,
plunged to her death off one of
the rocks there. And someone said,
"Hearn might be the rebirth of Sappho"—although I cannot be sure
of such an idea.

There are resemblances between
Hearn's picture, "The Eagle," and
the rocky picture of the *kakemono.* I
suppose my father had always in his
mind the scene of the rocky island,
Leucadia, where he was born. Although he left there in childhood, the
bright colorful beauty of the island
might have impressed itself into his
imagination. After the death of my
mother, I let my late brother Iwao
keep the *kakemono.* He wished for
it eagerly because his name, Iwao,
means a rock. . . . My name, Kazuo,
or Kajiwo, was taken from the sound
of Lafcadio.

---

[1] Setsuko Koizumi (Mrs. Lafcadio Hearn), *Reminiscences of Lafcadio Hearn;* trans. from the Japanese by Paul Kiyoshi Hisada and Frederick Johnson
(Boston: Houghton Mifflin Company, 1918), p. 79.

THE OWL

When cats run home and light is come,
  And dew is cold upon the ground,
And the far-off stream is dumb,
  And the whirring sail goes round,
  And the whirring sail goes round;
    Alone and warming his five wits,
    The white owl in the belfry sits.

When merry milkmaids click the latch,
  And rarely smells the new-mown hay,
And the cock hath sung beneath the thatch
  Twice or thrice his roundelay,
  Twice or thrice his roundelay;
    Alone and warming his five wits,
    The white owl in the belfry sits.

SECOND SONG TO THE SAME

Thy tuwhits are lull'd, I wot,
  Thy tuwhoos of yesternight,
Which upon the dark afloat,
  So took echo with delight,
  So took echo with delight;
    That her voice untuneful grown
    Wears all day a fainter tone.

I would mock thy chaunt anew;
  But I cannot mimic it;
Not a whit of thy tuwhoo,
  Thee to woo to thy tuwhit,
  Thee to woo to thy tuwhit,
    With a lengthen'd loud halloo,
    Tuwhoo, tuwhit, tuwhit, tuwhoo-o-o!
      ALFRED LORD TENNYSON

ABOUT THE OWL

Frequently I asked my father about the owl and he told me many interesting stories about it. The mystic owl is the bird of which I am most fond, though in China he was detested as a guilty bird. And in Japan he was treated as a magical bird which frightened people.

Besides the short-eared owl, I am fond of the long-eared rabbit or hare, and I often asked my parents to keep a rabbit for me.

One day, after he taught me Tennyson's poem, "The Owl," Father gave me this picture, but I don't know if this is a picture of his imagination or a copy from some book's

illustration. American youngsters may see a resemblance to the drawings of Walt Disney. But, of course, my father died before Walt Disney drew.

And, you know, if you speak this poem out loud you may sound like an owl! "Tuwhit, Tuwhoo-o-o."

THE THREE FISHERS

I

"Three fishers went sailing away to the West,
    Away to the West as the sun went down;
Each thought on the woman who loved him the best,
    And the children stood watching them out of the town;
    For men must work, and women must weep,
    And there's little to earn, and many to keep,
      Though the harbour bar be moaning."

II

"Three wives sat up in the lighthouse tower,
    And they trimmed the lamps as the sun went down;
And they looked at the squall, and they looked at the shower,
    And the night-rack came rolling up ragged and brown.
    But men must work, and women must weep,
    Though storms be sudden, and waters deep,
      And the harbour bar be moaning."

III

"Three corpses lay out on the shining sands
    In the morning gleam as the tide went down,
And the women are weeping and wringing their hands
    For those who will never come home to the town;
    For men must work, and women must weep,
    And the sooner it's over, the sooner to sleep;
      And good-bye to the bar and its moaning."

CHARLES KINGSLEY

Three fishers went sailing away to the West
Away to the West, as the sun went down,
Each thought on the woman who loved him best,
And the children stood watching them out of the town:
   For men must work, and women must weep,
   And there's little to earn, and many to keep,
      Though the harbour-bar be moaning.

CHARLES KINGSLEY—
ANOTHER ENGLISHMAN

"The Three Fishers"

Father gave me "The Three Fishers," by Charles Kingsley, as an English lesson at Yaidzu. It was the summer of 1900. We were living at the seaside place, in the upstairs room of the fishmonger Otokichi's house. Father painted for me these three pictures in three days—each day one picture for each stanza. (See page 41.)

After my daily English lesson was done, my father took out the color box and asked me to bring some water to paint the picture. When I went to fetch a saucer of water, my brother and a neighborhood boy noticed that I was through with my studies. They followed me to Father.

In the picture for the first stanza there are four boats. I suppose the shape of these boats does not look like Occidental fishing boats because they are Yaidzu fishing boats. At first Father put only one boat upon the horizon, but I wanted him to put more. He was slightly hesitant, but he added another. "Where is *my* boat?" my younger brother suddenly exclaimed. (Iwao was standing beside me.) "One is Papa's and another is for *Niisan* ('elder brother'), but there's none for me," he said.

Our friend Zensaku was near us,

looking at the picture; he is a fisherman's boy w h o s e face, Father thought, would be just suited for a Jizō model. "Papa, may you add one more boat for Zensaku-chan?" He nodded, and again he added a boat. When I turned to my friend I found his face was very bright as he peered into the picture.

After Father finished his painting he said, "This picture is not a sufficient expression of 'The Three Fishers.' This is far from my desire— this is only the sketch of Yaidzu-sea."

"Then," I said, "please write the poem of 'The Three Fishers' on the picture to explain this view is not just a view of Yaidzu-sea." My reply made Father burst into laughter, and he wrote the first stanza of "The Three Fishers" upon the picture.

The next day, after my study was over, Father began to draw a picture of the second stanza—a picture of a lighthouse tower.

While watching his drawings, we children chattered so much that he misdrew. He blamed us, took another paper and drew a lighthouse tower more carefully. He cut it out and pasted the lighthouse tower upon the former paper, on which he had painted the scene of dark sea and "the night-rack came rolling up ragged and brown." This time Father drew three boats for us sailing far off on the horizon. Also look for the wives waiting for their husbands in the tower.

You will find under the sepia clouds some aircraft-like things soaring. They are only sea gulls. I am glad to say that in neither Kingsley's nor Hearn's time were there B-29's or terrible Atomic Bombs.

While he painted the third picture only I was beside him. But he said "Don't come so close and peer at. . . ." When he was finished he showed it to me and asked with a queer smile, "What do you think?" I gazed at these faces of the three corpses who lay out on the shining sands. I exclaimed, "They are Papa, Iwao, and I!"

LONGFELLOW—AN AMERICAN

"THE LEAP OF ROUSHAN BEG"

This was d r a w n when Father taught me the Longfellow poem, "The Leap of Roushan Beg." He wanted me to understand the word "precipice." It was drawn in 1901 and he made use of the blank space of his draft for "In a Cup of Tea," which he published in *Kottō*.

THE LEAP OF ROUSHAN BEG

Mounted on Kyrat strong and fleet,
His chestnut steed with four white feet,
    Roushan Beg, called Kurroglou,
Son of the road and bandit chief,
Seeking refuge and relief,
    Up the mountain pathway flew. . . .

Suddenly, the pathway ends,
Sheer the precipice descends,
    Loud the torrent roars unseen;
Thirty feet from side to side
Yawns the chasm; on air must ride
    He who crosses this ravine.

Following close in his pursuit,
At the precipice's foot,
    Reyhan the Arab of Orfah
Halted with his hundred men,
Shouting upward from the glen,
    "La Illáh illa Alláh! . . ."

Kyrat, then, the strong and fleet,
Drew together his four white feet,
    Paused a moment on the verge,
Measured with his eye the space
And into the air's embrace,
    Leaped, as leaps the ocean surge.

As the ocean surge o'er sand
Bears a swimmer safe to land,
    Kyrat safe his rider bore;

Rattling down the deep abyss,
Fragments of the precipice
    Rolled like pebbles on a shore. . . .

Reyhan the Arab held his breath
While this vision of life and death
    Passed above him. "Allahu!"
Cried he. "In all Koordistan
Lives there not so brave a man
    As this robber Korroglou!"
                HENRY WADSWORTH LONGFELLOW

THOMAS MOORE—AN
IRISHMAN

SWAMP CYPRESS

This picture was drawn when
Father lectured to me on a ballad
of Thomas Moore's "The Lake of

the Dismal Swamp." He took out
one of his rough drafts. This rough
draft was of the "Story of Mimi-
nashi-Hoichi," from his book *Kwaidan*. It was in the heap of writing
papers which were on the left side
of his big working desk. Drawn on
the margin were the explanations of
a paddle and a canoe. Then he
turned to the reverse side and drew
this picture of a swamp cypress.

THE LAKE OF THE DISMAL SWAMP

(Written at Norfolk, in Virginia)

"They tell of a young man, who lost his
mind upon the death of a girl he loved, and
who, suddenly disappearing from his friends,
was never afterwards heard of. As he had
frequently said, in his ravings, that the
girl was not dead, but gone to the Dismal
Swamp, it is supposed he had wandered into that dreary wilderness, and died of hun-
ger, or been lost in some of its dreadful
morasses."

                                ANONYMOUS

"La Poésie a ses monstres comme la nature."

                                D'ALEMBERT

They made her a grave, too cold and damp
    For a soul so warm and true;
And she's gone to the Lake of the Dismal
        Swamp,
Where, all night long, by a fire-fly lamp,
    She paddles her white canoe.

And her fire-fly lamp I soon shall see,
    And her paddle I soon shall hear;
Long and loving our life shall be,
And I'll hide the maid in a cypress tree
    When the footstep of Death is near!

Away to the Dismal Swamp he speeds—
  His path was rugged and sore,
Through tangled juniper, beds of reeds,
Through many a fen where the serpent feeds,
  And man never trod before!

And, when on the earth he sunk to sleep,
  If slumber his eyelids knew,
He lay, where the deadly vine doth weep
Its venomous tear and nightly steep
  The flesh with blistering dew!

And near him the she-wolf stirr'd the brake,
  And the copper-snake breathed in his ear,
Till he starting cried, from his dream awake,
"Oh! when shall I see the dusky Lake,
  And the white canoe of my dear?"

He saw the Lake, and a meteor bright
  Quick over its surface played—
"Welcome," he said, "my dear one's light!"
And the dim shore echoed, for many a night,
  The name of the death-cold maid!

Till he hollow'd a boat of the birchen bark,
  Which carried him off from shore;
Far, far he follow'd the meteor spark,
The wind was high and the clouds were dark,
  And the boat return'd no more.

But oft, from the Indian hunter's camp,
  This lover and maid so true
Are seen at the hour of midnight damp
To cross the Lake by a fire-fly lamp,
  And paddle their white canoe!

THOMAS MOORE

HANS CHRISTIAN ANDERSEN —A DANE

Father gave me Hans Christian Andersen's "The Little Mermaid" to read. To describe the cracking sound of the icebergs, Father used the same sound that the Greek playwright, Aristophanes, used for his chorus in *The Frogs*—"Krek-kek-ko-ax! Ko-ax!"

THE DRAIN, CANAL, ARCH AND GUTTER

When Father gave me Hans Christian Andersen's "The Constant Tin

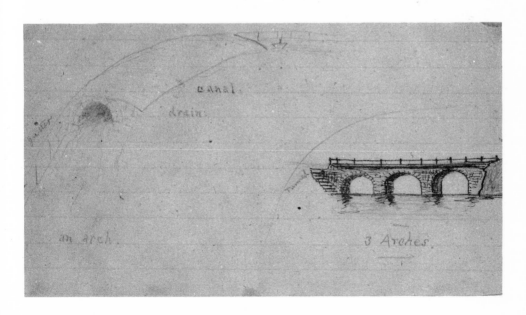

Soldier" to read, he taught me these words: "drain," "canal," "arch," and "gutter." And he drew these pictures for me.

You may remember that in the story two boys put the Tin Soldier into a boat made of newspaper and sent him sailing down a *gutter*. Although the current was strong and the journey rough, the Tin Soldier did not let fear overcome him.

Then the boat went into a *drain,* and darkness was all around. The Tin Soldier wondered where he was and wished that the little lady might be with him. Then he would not mind the darkness!

A tremendous water rat loomed up and asked the Tin Soldier for his pass. Having none, the Tin Soldier silently gripped his musket with all his might. The water rat rushed after the boat, yelling to hold the Tin Soldier for not having paid his toll or shown his pass.

Finally, up ahead, the Tin Soldier could see an *arch* and bright daylight at the end of the tunnel. But there was still danger ahead, for the *drain* led into an enormous *canal*. And for the Tin Soldier in his boat —a newspaper—this was bound to be an adventure!

A GALLOWS

When Father gave me Hans Christian Andersen's "The Tinder-Box"

to read, there came the word "gallows." Then he took a pencil and drew this picture on his pocket

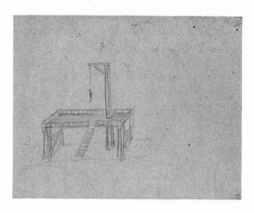

notebook for me. Unlike the man in the picture, the soldier in the story was not hanged. I was glad.

In my childhood I was only amused by the various actions in this story. But nowadays, each time I reread "The Tinder-Box," it gives me a new interest.

THE BIBLE

FROM THE BOOK OF JOHN AND THE BOOK OF JOB

This picture I found in his old pocket notebook on which the title leaf read: "Lafcadio Hearn with a *Bon Voyage* from his friends Daniel and Alice Rollins." The fine handwriting was dated March, 1890. Father arrived in Japan in April, 1890. Mrs. Rollins was one of Father's friends in New York.

The picture might be a sketch

which he made on his last journey in America. He later wrote about the Rockies:

Above all, one pyramidal peak, ghost-white as the Throne of the Vision of John, ever lifts itself higher behind us as we flee away. Again and again the road turns in vast spirals as we circle the hills: we thunder through long chasms and pass continually from sun to shadow and from shadow to sun; and other mountains interpose their white heads, their spruce—and that marvellous shape—ever heaping themselves in huger maze behind us. But still, over them all, shines the eternal white peace of that supremest peak,—growing ever taller to look down upon us,—to mock our feverish hurrying with the perpetual solemnity of its snowy rest. And watching it, there returns to me with a sudden new strange pleasure, as of fancied revelation in slumber, the words of Job:—"He maketh peace in his high places. . . ."[2]

2 Lafcadio Hearn, "A Winter Journey to Japan," *Harper's Magazine,* November, 1890.

Off to Other Worlds---
Lessons

GEOGRAPHY

Father dictated geography lessons to me and I wrote them in my tablet which we called Kazuo's Copybook. He used this method to teach me and also to improve my penmanship. Of course, some of the information is now out of date. But I think Father's dictations to me disclose a good grasp of the world.

There are five great oceans—the Pacific Ocean, the Atlantic Ocean, the Indian Ocean, the Arctic Ocean, and the Antarctic Ocean. And there are five great divisions of land, called continents: their names are Europe, Asia, Africa, America, and Australia.

The names of the principal countries of Europe are:—

Great Britain (including England, Ireland, Scotland, and Wales).

France, Spain, Italy, Portugal, Greece, Turkey in Europe (all southern).

Germany, Holland, Belgium, Denmark, Sweden, Norway, and Russia (all northern).

Switzerland, Austria, Hungary, Bulgaria, Servia, and Roumania (all central).

There are also some very small countries —such as Montenegro and Monaco.

AFRICA

The great country of Africa is the country of the black people, called Negroes. The hair of negro-people is curly, like the wool of a black sheep.

But all the people living in Africa are not negroes. There are brown people in the north of Africa;—some are Arabs; some are Egyptians. Also you must remember that the English people, and French people, and German people and Belgian people, all have taken some land along the sea-shore.

A great part of Africa, in the north is a desert. The name of this enormous desert is The Sahara. It is like the bottom of a dried-up sea—all rocks and sand. When a great storm comes, the sand moves like the waves of an ocean, and smothers men and horses and camels. And, in ancient times, whole armies of soldiers were swallowed up by that sand. So the desert is full of the bones of dead men.

Now in the great sea of sand, there are many islands, where trees grow, and where villages are built. By travelling from one island to another island, people are able to cross the Sahara:—these islands are called "oases." The singular of the word is "oasis."

In the desert there are no rivers or lakes. But people travelling there sometimes think that they see beautiful lakes, with trees, and they try to go to the water. But when they get to the place, there is no water, nor any trees—nothing but dry hot sand, and dead men's bones. This ghostly sight is called a *mirage*.

In Africa there are many wonderful creatures—lions, ostriches, gorillas, crocodiles, and hyaenas. Some of these live in the desert —especially lions and ostriches.

Now I am going to tell you a story about a lion of the desert. There was a young woman who lost her way in the desert. A lion came to her and said, "Do not be afraid; come with me." The woman followed the lion. And the lion led that woman to a cave, where he fed her every day for two weeks. After that time, he took her back to her own village, and left her there.

Her father and her mother and her brothers and sisters were very happy to see her again; and they wondered at her story. They asked her if the lion had been kind to her; and she answered:—

"Yes,—but his breath stinks horribly!"

As she said these words, there was an awful roar outside—the lion had been listening.

Some days after, when that woman was all alone, the lion came to her and said:—

"Do you see that mark of a spear on my breast?"

The woman looked, and said:—

"Yes—but the wound is quite healed."

"Quite healed—are you sure?" asked the lion.

"Oh, yes," answered she.

"That was the wound of a spear only," said the lion. "The wound of a spear soon heals; but the wound made by [the] tongue never heals." And he devoured that woman.

Here is a story about an animal more clever than a woman!

The Lion, the King of Beasts, once got sick. He thought that his breath was bad. But he could not smell his own breath. So he called the Bear, and said; "Mr. Bear, please smell my breath, and tell me if it is bad. Tell me the truth!"

The Bear always tells the truth. But he is not polite. He is the most rude of all animals. He put his nose to the Lion's mouth, and said;—

"Phew!—your breath stinks worse than a dead dog!"

The Lion became very angry at these words. He gave one terrible roar, and jumped at the Bear, and killed him, and ate him up, because he was rude. Then he called the Monkey, and said:—"Smell my breath, and tell me if it is bad."

The Monkey was afraid, because he had seen the Bear killed. So he determined to tell a lie. He smelled the Lion's breath, and cried:—

"Oh! how good!—oh! how nice, how sweet! Better than roses!—better than musk, sweeter than incense! Please let me smell it again!"

Then the Lion became very angry, because he knew that the Monkey wished to flatter him. He killed the Monkey, ate him, and called the Fox.

The Fox is not a fool. He is cunning.

The Fox smelled the Lion's breath and said nothing. He smelled it again, and said nothing. Once more he put his nose to the Lion's mouth. And then he said:—

"Excuse me! Last night I caught a very bad cold, and today I cannot smell anything."

The highest mountains in the world are in the north of India, and are called the Himalayas; the name of the highest of them is Mount Everest.

It is nearly 30,000 feet high. Mount Fuji is only 12,365 feet high—so Mount Everest is more than twice as high as the highest mountain of Japan. It is five and a half miles high,—English miles.

Two and a half English miles make one Japanese *ri*. So Mount Everest is more than two *ri* high. The height of any mountain is measured from the surface of the sea.

There are also in South America very high mountains—many of them more than four miles high, or twice as high as Fuji. The highest is 24,812 feet high.

In South America there are more than fifty volcanoes. Some of them are 20,000 feet high;—some are even higher.

As we climb a mountain, we find that the air becomes thinner and colder. At the height of Fuji, the air is always as cold as in mid-winter in Tōkyō. But at the height of 20,000 feet, the air is so cold and thin that blood flows from the ears and mouth. So men cannot climb to the top of the highest mountains.

The most awful volcano in the world is Cotopaxi, in South America. It is much higher than Fuji; and its roaring can be heard hundreds of miles away.

A long line of mountains, standing close together, is called a chain, or range, or, sometimes, a sierra—which word is Spanish. The longest range of mountains in the world are the Andes, in South America;—they are 4,500 miles long.

The deep[e]st water in the world is, perhaps, in the Pacific Ocean, near the north of Japan. There the sea is 27,930 feet—or five miles and a quarter (5¼) [deep];—that is, nearly as deep as the Himalaya Mountains are high. But there is. a place near the West Indies, in the Atlantic Ocean, which is almost as deep—27,366 feet. Perhaps there are much deeper places in the cold Antarctic Ocean; but we do not yet know. The deepest place known is northeast of Japan.

The longest and widest and deepest river in the world is the Amazon, in South America. So great a river is it that, before the mouth of it, for a distance of fifty miles the sea is fresh water. Great steamers go up the Amazon for a distance of 1,500 miles; but the Amazon is really 4,000 miles long.

ABOUT NORTH AMERICA

Today we shall talk about North America. At dinner-time you saw a tin can full of salmon. It came from the country called Alaska, in northwestern America. That country used to belong to Russia; but Russia sold it to the United States. It is a very large country;—there are many great rivers and lakes and frostes [forests] there, and plenty of gold and silver, and plenty of white bears and white foxes and blue foxes. But it is very, very, very cold.

East of Alaska is the great country of Canada. Canada belongs to England; and most of the people speak English. But Canada used to belong to France;—so the people in many places also speak French.

Under Canada you will see, on the map, a very great country called the United States. Next to Russia, it is the biggest country in the world; and [,] except England, it is the richest country in the world. English is the language of the United States. The people have no king or emperor;—they have only a President; and he rules for only four years. Every four years there is a new President.

When you look at a map of the United States, you will find that there are 44 states. That is why there are 44 stars on the flag of the United States. There are allso on the flag thirteen stripes—red and white. Those thirteen states used to belong to England; but, a little more than a hundred years ago, they made war against England, and became free. Many black people also live in the United States; they are negroes, whose ancestors came from Africa, and were sold for slaves.

South of the United States lies the great and beautiful country called Mexico. [The] language of Mexico is Spanish. The people of Mexico have no king; they govern themselves, like the people of the United States. A country where the people govern themselves is called a republic. I want to tell you also that the Mexicans make very pretty pictures with the feathers of little birds.

CENTRAL AMERICA

South from Mexico begins Central America. Central America is all one isthmus. This is the hottest part of America—perhaps of the world. But there are six different countries in Central America. One belongs to England, and is called Belize, or British Honduras. And the names of the other five countries are, Honduras, Nicaragua, Salvador, Guatemala, and Costa-Rica, —all republics.

Just south of Costa Rica is the famous isthmus of Panama. One side is washed by the Pacific Ocean, and the other side by the Atlantic Ocean. Here is the narrowest part of America; and there is a railroad across it. But, in order that ships may pass from one Ocean to the other, a great canal will soon be dug across the Isthmus of Panama. It will be called the Panama Canal.

SOUTH AMERICA

South of the famous isthmus of Panama is the Republic of Colombia. With Colombia, South America begins. Next to Colombia, eastward, is the Republic of Venezuela.

Next to Venezuela are three countries called, British Guiana, French Guiana, and Dutch Guiana. These three countries belong[,] Respectively, to England, Holland, and France.

The other countries of South America are Brazil, Ecuador, Peru, Bolivia, Chile, Paraguay, Uruguay, and the Argentine Republic, with Patagonia.

Brazil is the largest country in south America. The people speak Portuguese. But in the rest of South America they speak Spanish.

Quito is said to be the highest city in the world.

ASIA

Now we must study the map of Asia. Asia is the largest of all the continents. All the northern part of Asia belongs to Russia; and it is called Asiatic Russia, or Russia in Asia. The most northern part of Asiatic Russia is called Siberia.

Now let us look at the Eastern part of the map. In the east is the grate [great] country of China—which contains more people than any other country in the world; for there are more than 400,000,000 of people in China. Four hundred million—[400,000,-000]—that is to say, four times more people than there are in the whole of great Russia. Do you know that the English call porcelain "china" because it was first made in China?

South of China there is a great country called Indo-China. It is called Indo-China because it is between India and China. In Indo-China there are many kingdoms. Burmah and Siam are the largest. Other states are Cambodia, Annam, Cochin-China, Tonking, and Laos. All these are governed or protected by France; but Burmah is protected by England.

South of Indo-China, there is a very long peninsula called the Malay Peninsula. It is divided into several states, which are protected by England. And at the southern end of the Malay Peninsula is the great port and city of Singapore—where the pineapples come from. Singapore belongs to England; but most of the merchants are Chinese.

West of China is Thibet:—it is a very high and cold country of mountains. And it is a very famous country—because it is a Buddhist country. The people have no king; but they are governed by priests—Buddhist priests.

South of Thibet is India—a very great country, containing more than one hundred and fifty millions of people. India belongs to England—all except a little bit, which is called Pondicherry, and which belongs to France. But there are still some Indian kings who are allowed to rual [rule] on condition that they obey the king of England. In India there are many elephants—tame and wild.

The Baby and the Serpent

In India there is a very poisonous serpent called the Cobra. If the Cobra bites anybody, that person must die. No doctor can save a person bitten by a Cobra. But sometimes the Cobra can be very gentle.

There was a little English boy in India who had a Cobra for a friend. As it is very hot in India, the little boy used to eat his breakfast in the garden. For breakfast he had bread and milk. One morning, while this little boy was eating his breakfast in the garden, his father was astonished and frightened to see his little son playing with a big cobra. The serpent was drinking milk and eating bread out of the child's bowl. First, the little boy would eat; then the cobra would eat;—and when the cobra ate too fast, the boy would hit it on the head with his spoon, and say, "Fie! don't be so greedy!" And sometimes the cobra would get angry and hiss.

When all the bread and milk had been finished, the serpent went away; and the little boy called after him: "Come back again tomorrow!"

But that cobra never came back again, because the little boy's father went after the creature immediately, and shot it dead with a gun.

And the little boy cried.

Once in India there were four brothers. Three of them were merchants, and made money. But the youngest did not like to be a merchant. He liked only to study magic; and he became a magician. His brothers were not pleased at this.

One day the four brothers were walking together on a lonesome road; and they saw the bones of a dead lion. The bones were old and dry, and white as snow.

Then the brother who was a magician, said:—

"Now I am going to show you a wonderful thing. I am going to make that dead lion become alive again."

"How can you do that?" the others asked. The magician answered:—

"When I speak three magical words, that lion will become alive again, and you will hear him roar."

"But that is a lion,—a LION!" said the second brother:—"Do not, I beg, speak those words."

At this, the other brothers all laughed; and the magician said;—

"If you are afraid, go home! I am going to talk to that lion." And he spoke the first magical word.

Immediately that he spoke the word, the white bones of the lion came together with a hard dry sound, and became jointed.

"Now," said the magician, "I shall speak the second word."

"My brother," said he who had spoken before, "do not say that word! A lion is a fearful thing! Do not say that word!"

"If you are afraid, go home!" again answered the magician. And he spoke the word.

And as soon as he spoke that second word, the white bones of the lion became covered with flesh, and muscles and skin, and hair. A monstrous lion!

my breast?"

The woman looked, and said:—

"Yes—but the wound is quite healed."

"Quite healed—are you sure?" asked the lion.

"Oh, yes," answered she.

"That was the wound of a spear only," said the lion. "The wound of a spear soon heals; but the wound made by tongue never heals." And he devoured that woman.

Second Lesson in Geography.

The highest highest mountains in the world are in the north of India, and are called the Himalayas. The name of the highest of them is Mount Everest. It is nearly 30,000 feet high. Mount Fuji is only

12,365 feet high—so Mount Everest is more than twice as high as the highest mountain of Japan. It is five and a half miles high—English miles. Two and a half English miles make one Japanese ri. So Mount Everest is more than two ri high. The height of any mountain is measured from the surface of the sea.

There are also in South America very high mountains—many of them more than four mi high, or twice as high as Fuji. The highest is 24,812 feet high.

(In South America there are more)
In South America there are more than fifty volcanoes. Some of them are than fifty volcanoes. Some of them are

20,000 feet high;—some are even higher.)
20,000 feet high;—some are even higher.
(As we climb a mountain, we find)
As we climb a mountain, we find
that the air becomes thinner and colder.)
that the air becomes thinner and colder.
At the height of Fuji, the air is always as cold
as in mid-winter in Tokyō. But at the height of
20,000 feet, the air is so cold and thin that blood
flows from the ears and mouth, so men cannot climb
to the top of the highest mountains.
The most awful volcano in the world is
Cotopaxi, in South America. It is much higher than
Fuji; and its roaring can be heard hundreds of miles away.
A long line of mountains, standing close

SIERRA

together, is called a chain, or range, or, sometimes, a sierra—which word is Spanish. The longest range of mountains in the world are the Andes, in South America; —they are 4,500 miles long.)

(The deepest water in the world is, perhaps, in the Pacific Ocean, near the north of Japan. There the sea is 27,930 feet—or five miles and a quarter ($5\frac{1}{4}$) deep;—that is, nearly as deep as the Himalaya Mountains are high. But there is a place near the West Indies, in the Atlantic Ocean, which is almost as deep—27,366 feet. Perhaps there are much deeper places in the cold Antarctic Ocean; but we do not yet know. The deepest place known is north-east of Japan.)

(The longest and widest and deepest river in the world is the Amazon, in South America. So great a river is it that, before the mouth of it, for a distance of fifty miles, the sea is fresh water. Great steamers go up the Amazon for a distance of 1,500 miles; but the Amazon is really 4,000 miles long.)

About North America

Today we shall talk about North America. At dinner-time you saw a tin can full of salmon. It came from the country called Alaska, in north-western America. That country used to belong to Russia; but Russia sold it to the United States. It is a very large country;—there are many great rivers and lakes and frosts there, and plenty of gold and silver, and plenty of white bears and white foxes and blue foxes. But it is very, very, very cold. East of Alaska is the great country of Canada. Canada belongs to England, and most of the people speak English. But Canada used to belong to France;—so the people in many places also speak French. Under Canada you will see, on the map, a very great country called the United States. Next to Russia, this is the biggest country in the world; and except England, it is the richest country in the world. English is the language of the United States. The people have no king or emperor; they have only a President; and he rules for only four years. Every four years there is a new President.

When you look at a map of the United States, you will find that there are 44 states. That is why there are 44 stars on the flag of the United States. There are also on the flag thirteen stripes—red and white. That is because at first there were only thirteen states. Those thirteen states used to belong to England; but, a little more than a hundred years ago, they made war against England, and became free. Many black people also live in the United States; they are negroes, whose ancestors came from Africa, and were sold for slaves.

South of the United States lies the great and beautiful country called Mexico. The language of Mexico is Spanish. The people of Mexico have no king; they govern themselves, like the people of the United States.

(A) country where the people govern themselves is called a republic. I want to tell you also that the Mexicans make very pretty pictures with the feathers of little birds.

Central America.

South from Mexico begins Central America. Central America is all one isthmus. This is the hottest part of America—perhaps of the world. But there are six different countries in Central America. One belongs to England, and is called Belize or British Honduras. And the names of the other five countries are, Honduras, Nicaragua, Salvador, Guatemala, and Costa-Rica—all republics.

Just south of Costa Rica is the famous isthmus of Panama. One side is washed by the Pacific

Ocean, and the other side by the Atlantic Ocean. Here is the narrowest part of America; and there is a railroad across it. But, in order that ships may pass from one Ocean to the other, a great canal will soon be dug across the Isthmus of Panama. It will be called the Panama Canal.

Little Prayer

Now I lay me down to sleep,
I pray the Lord my soul to keep;
And if I die before I wake,
I pray the Lord my soul to take.)

South America.

South of the famous isthmus of Panama is the Republic of Colombia. With Colombia, South America begins. Next to Colombia eastward, is the Republic of Venezuela. Next to Venezuela are three countries called, British Guiana, French Guiana, and Dutch Guiana. These three countries belong respectively to England, Holland, and France. The other countries of South America are Brazil, Ecuador, Peru, Bolivia, Chile, Paraguay, Uruguay, and the Argentine Republic, that with Patagonia.

Brazil is the largest country in south America. The people speak Portuguese. But in the rest of South

America they speak Spanish. Quito is said to be the highest city in the world.

Open the gates as high as the sky
To let King George's men go by.

Open the gates as high as the sky
To let King George's men go by.

There was a little girl,
And she had a little curl
Right in the middle of her forehead;
When she was good, she was very, very good,
And when she was bad, she was horrid.

Four ducks on a pond,
A grass-bank beyond,
A blue sky of spring,
White clouds on the wing—
What a little thing
To remember for years,
To remember with tears!

Asia.

Now we must study the map of Asia.
Now we must study the map of Asia.
Asia is the largest of all the continents.
Asia is the largest of all the continents.
All the northern part of Asia belongs
All the northern part of Asia belongs

to Russia; and it is called Asiatic
to Russia; and it is called Asiatic
Russia, or Russia in Asia. The most
Russia, or Russia in Asia. The most
northern part of Asiatic Russia is called
northern part of Asiatic Russia is called
Siberia.)
Siberia.

(Now let us look at the Eastern part of the
map. In the east is the great country of
China—which contains more people than any other
country in the world. for there are more than 400,000,000
people in China. Do you know that the English call
porcelain "china"—because it was first made in China.

Four hundred millions   Four hundred millions   Four hundred millions [400,000,000] — that is to say, four times more people than there are in the whole of great Russia.

South of China there is a great country called Indo-China. It is called Indo-China because it is between India and China. In Indo-China there are many kingdoms. Burmah and Siam are the largest. Other states are Cambodia, Annam, Cochin-China, Tonking, and Laos. All these are governed or protected by France; but Burmah is protected by England.

South of Indo-China there is a very long peninsula called the Malay Peninsula. It is divided into several states, which are protected by England. And at the southern end of the Malay Peninsula is

the great port and city of Singapore— where the pine
apples come from. Singapore belongs to England; but
most of the merchants are Chinese).

West of China is Thibet: it is — it is a very high
and cold country of mountains. And it is a very
famous country—because it is a Buddhist country
the people have no king; but they are governed by
priests— Buddhist priests.

South of Thibet is India — a very great country
containing more than one hundred and fifty million
of people. India belongs to England—all except a little
bit, which is called Pondicherry, and which belongs to
France. But there are still some Indian kings who are
allowed to rule on condition that they obey the king of England
In India there are many elephants—tame and wild—)

To the north-west of India beyond the mountains is the country of Afghanistan. This too country has its own ruler. And the people are very fierce.

Next to Afghanistan, on the west side, is the great country of Persia. Its king is called the Shah.

Next to Persia, on the west side, is Turkey in Asia— also called Asia Minor. Asia Minor. Asia Minor. Asia Minor contains (the famous country of Palestine, and the (the famous country of Palestine, and the (city of Jerusalem. And here also is) city of Jerusalem. And here also is (the country of Syria. The capital of) the country of Syria. The capital of

(Syria is Smyrna. Papa's mother used)
Syria is Smyrna. Papa's mother used
(to live at Smyrna.)
to live at Smyrna.
(And south of all this Turkish)
And south of all this Turkish
(country is famous Arabia.)
country is famous Arabia.

(Little drops of water,)
Little grains of sand,
Make the mighty ocean,
And the pleasant land.)

(I never had a piece of bread
Particularly long and wide,
But on the floor 'twas sure to fall,
And always on the buttered side.

Islands.

There are only five continents in the world—or perhaps six; because there may the be an Antarctic continent. But there are many thousands of islands.

Most islands are gathered together in groups; and if we learn the names of the groups—then we shall be able to remember the names of the islands.

A group of islands is called an archipelago.

(The Empire of Japan is an archipelago; for it is made of many islands close together. Great Britain is an archipelago.

The biggest archipelago in the world is the Malay Archipelago which is south and west of the Malay Peninsula. It contains many very large islands, such as Sumatra, Java, Borneo Celebes, New Guinea, Timor, &c. Java is famous for coffee and black tigers. Earthquakes are very terrible in Java; and there are thirty volcanoes.

The Malay Archipelago belongs mostly to Holland; but the English own part of Borneo. North of Borneo are the Philippine Islands which no belong to the United States. The Capital is Manila — famous for coffee and tobacco — especially cigars.)

South of the Malay Archipelago is the largest island in the world—so large that we call it a continent Australia. It belongs to England. And East of Australia there are two large and beautiful islands called New Zealand—also English. New Zealand is cool, and very pleasant. The country once belonged to savages who were cannibals. But now there are not many savages; and most of the people are English. Many of the savage women married English men.

This world is all a fleeting show,
~For Man's illusion given;
The smiles of joy, the tears of woe,
Deceitful shine, deceitful flow,—
There's nothing true but Heaven!

(Now look at the map of India. At the south of India you will see a very large island called Ceylon. That island is famous for elephants. The wild elephants are caught by tame elephants. Now look at the map of Africa. At the south-east of Africa you will see a very long and large island called Madagascar. That great island belongs to France. The people are black, but not ugly. The climate is very hot. Madagascar is the third largest island in the world. Near Madagascar there are two islands, one of which belongs to England, and one to France.)

(He saith among the trumpets, Ha, ha; and he smelleth the battle afar off, the thunder of the captains, and the shouting.

Geography—continued.

South of Australia there is a large island called Tasmania. It belongs to England. Before the English came to these countries, Australia and Tasmania were inhabited by black people who were very skillful at throwing crooked sticks, called boomerangs. When these boomerangs were thrown, they would go far away along the ground, and then rise straight up into the sky and then come back again.)

I once had a sweet little doll, dears,
  The prettiest doll in the world;
Her cheeks were so red and so white, dears,
  And her hair was so charmingly curled.
But I lost my poor little doll, dears,
  As I played on the heath one day;
And I cried for more than a week, dears,
  But I never could find where she lay.

I found my poor little doll, dears,
  As I played in the heath one day.
Folks say she is terribly changed, dears,
  For her paint is all washed away,
And her arms trodden off by the cows, dears,

And her hair not the least bit curled;
But for old sake's sake she is still, dear
The prettiest doll in the world.

Geography — continued.

The West Indies, or West Indian Islands, is a
very great archipelago on the east side of
Central America. It contains more than three
hundred islands; the Principal islands are Cuba,
Jamaica, Porto Rico, and San Domingo. The capita
of Cuba is Havana — famous for cigars.)

"Now," said the magician, "when I speak the third word, that lion will become alive."

"Please wait just one minute," said the man who was afraid. "Before you say that word, please let me climb up this tree!"

Everybody laughed; and the man climbed the tree. Then the magician spoke the word.

Immediately that he spoke it, the lion opened his big yellow eyes, and roared like thunder, so that the ground shook. Then he sprang at the three men before him, and crushed them, and devoured them, bones and all.

But the man in the tree was not hurt. When the lion was gone[,] that man ran home.

To the north-west of India beyond the mountains, is the country of Afghanistan. This country has its own khis [king]. And the people are very fierce.

Next to Afghanistan, on the west side, is the great country of Persia. Its king is called the Shah. Next to Persia, on the west side, is Turkey in Asia—also called Asia Minor. Asia Minor contains the famous country of Palestine, and the city of Jerusalem. And here also is the country of Syria. The capital of Syria is Smyrna. Papa's mother used to live at Smyrna.

And south of all this Turkish country is famous Arabia.

ISLANDS

There are only five continents in the world—or perhaps six; because there may be an Antarctic continent. But there are many thousands of islands.

Most islands are gathered together in groups; and if we learn the names of the groups—then we shall be able to remember the names of the islands.

A group of islands is called an archipelago.

The Empire of Japan is an archipelago; for it is made of many islands close together. Great Britain is an archipelago.

The biggest archipelago in the world is the Malay Archipelago which is south and west of the Malay Peninsula. It contains many very large islands, such as Sumatra, Java, Borneo, Celebes, New Guinea, Timor, &c. Java is famous for coffee and black tigers. Earthquakes are very terrible in Java; and there are thirty volcanoes.

The Malay Archipelago belongs mostly to Holland; but the English own part of Borneo. North of Borneo are the Philippine Islands which now belong to the United States. The Capital is Manila—famous for coffee and tobacco,—especially cigars.

So[u]th of the Malay Archipelago is the largest island in the world—so large that we call it a continent: Australia. It belongs to England. And east of Australia there are two large and beautiful islands called New Zealand—also English.

New Zealand is cool, and very pleasant. The country once belonged to savages who weare [were] cannibals. But now theare [there] are not many savages; and most of the people are English. Many of the savage women married English men.

Now look at the map of India. At the south of India you will see a very large island called Ceylon. That island is famous for elephants. The wild elephants are caught by tame elephants.

Now look at the map of Africa. At the south-east of Africa you will see a very long and large island called Madagascar. That great island belongs to France. The people are black, but not ugly. The climate is very hot. Madagascar is the third largest island in the world. Near Madagascar there are two islands, one of which belongs to England, and one to France.

South of Australia there is a large island called Tasmania. It belongs to England.

Before the English came to these countries, Australia and Tasmania were inhabited by black people who were very skillful at throwing crooked sticks, called boomerangs. When these boomerangs were thrown, they would go far away along the ground and then rise straight up into the sky and then come back again.

The West Indies, or West Indian Islands, is a very great archipelago on the east side of Central America. It contains more than three hundred islands: the Principal islands are Cuba, Jamaica, Porto Rico, and San Domingo.

The capital of Cuba is Havana—famous for cigars.

THE PORT

This might be a sketch of the Port of St. Pierre. I found it between Father's old manuscripts and photographs of Martinique in the French West Indies. We can imagine by these schooners and pirogues, the shipment of molasses, rum, and some other goods. He never signed his drawings. But on this sketch in the right side downward, I can see some letters, not clear, but it is possible to read the faint sign, "L. Hearn." It seems that he once signed but, afterwards, he rubbed it off because of his shyness.

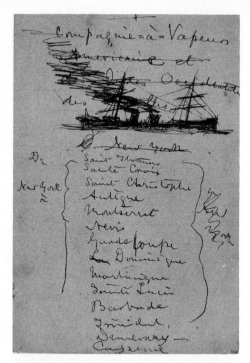

THE STEAMER

I found this pen sketch on the top page of his pocket notebook in which he had written many memos about the Windward Island. I suppose he took the trip to the French West Indies in such a steamer, named the *Barracouta*.

LA MONTAGNE PELÉE

Found in his old pocket notebook, this rough sketch might have been drawn in 1888, under the bright and dazzling hot sunshine of the mysterious Martinique Island. In this drawing, he used two pencils, black and purple.

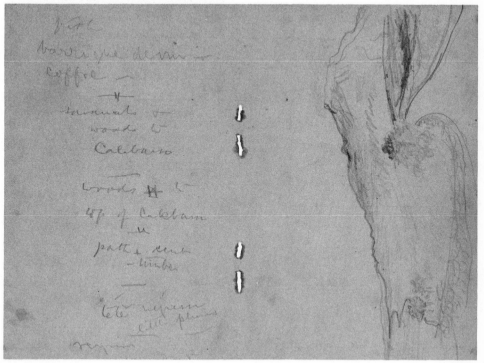

NATURAL HISTORY

Father dictated lessons in natural history for my Copybook.

The study of the life and habits of beasts, birds, fishes, insects, and plants, is called Natural History. A person who studies and teaches these things is called a naturalist. I hope that my dear little boy will become a good naturalist, and a wise teacher.

But there is no living man who can learn the whole of Natural History. So one man studies only insects, and another only plants, and another only birds[,] and so forth.

REPTILES

There are many different kinds of creatures. But all creatures are either cold-blooded or warm-blooded animals. All animals that have milk are warm-blooded. And birds are warm-blooded, although they have no milk. But fishes, snakes, insects, frogs, lizards are cold-blooded animals.

Of these, all snakes and frogs and lizards are called reptiles.

All reptiles are born from eggs: lizards, frogs, and serpents lay eggs. All reptiles have bones. Tortoises also are reptiles.

WHAT THE AIR IS MADE OF

When we begin attentively to consider the world around us, one of the first things to claim notice is the air. We do not see it, and yet it is present wherever we may go. How profoundly it influences the life of man!

Swinging your arm rapidly up and down you feel that the air offers a resistance to the hand. The air is something which one can feel, though one cannot see it. We breathe it every moment. We cannot get away from it, for it completely surrounds the earth as an envelope fifty miles or more in depth.

Air is a mixture if two invisible gases, called *nitrogen* and *oxygen*. It contains also small quantities of other substances— some of which are visible, others invisible.

THE CONDOR

The Condor is the largest of all flying birds. There are bigger birds which do not fly; but the Condor is larger than any eagle. It is somewhat like a very big kite.

The Condor lives only in South America, on the tops of the high mountains. It can sleep in the sky, floating upon its wings in the air; and it flies so high that nobody can shoot it.

The Condor kills a great many sheep and calves; and[,] therefore[,] the government gives a reward to anybody who kills a Condor. But the only way to kill a Condor is to catch it in a trap.

QUEER PLANTS

There are queer plants that catch flies. Their leaves are almost like hands. On the upper side of the leaves there is something sweet and sticky, like honey. Flies like sweet things. So they go on the leaves of these plants.

The body of a fly, caught in this way, melts inside the leaf.

ABOUT CRABS

There are crabs which eat men. These are land-crabs. They are not very big. They live near the sea-shore in hot countries. If a man goes there alone millions of crabs attack him, and bite him and tear him, and gnaw the flesh from all his bones,—as the rats devoured Bishop Hatto.[1]

Some crabs have only one pair of claws, or pincers, or nippers. But this single craw, [claw], or nipper, is as big as the crab's whole body. And people call these crabs fiddler-crabs because they look like fiddlers carrying fiddles.

Every year the crab gets a new shell:—

---

[1] In allusion to a ballad by Robert Southey, "God's Judgment on a Wicked Bishop."

the new shell is very soft, and while the crab remains soft, it is called a soft-shell[ed] crab. Soft-shell[ed] crabs, if well cooked, are very good to eat.

Some crabs eat poisonous fruits. In the West Indies there is a tree called the ma[n]chineel-tree, and it bears beautiful red apples. But if you taste those beautiful fruits, you will die. And the wood of the tree, and the bark, and the leaves are so poisonous that you cannot touch them, [or] the skin comes off your hands. Even the shadow of the tree is poisonous. But crabs live in holes under the roots, and eat the poisonous fruits.

THE NAMES OF THE DAYS

The first day of the week is called Sunday,—that means the Day of the Sun. The ancient English worshipped the Sun; and the name of the Sun-god was Balder. Balder was the most beautiful of the gods.

Monday means "Moon-Day," or the Day of the Moon:—people used to worship the God of the Moon on that day. And the word Month, meaning the time of one moon, means also the time of thirty days, from new moon to new moon.

Tuesday means the Day of the God Tiw, and used to be spelled Tiwesday. This god Tiw, or Tyr, as some people called him, was the bravest of all the northern gods. Someday I will read you a wonderful story about him.

Wednesday means "Woden's Day",—the day of Woden or Odin, as he was called in the far North. Odin was the father of all the gods and the wisest of them. He had only one eye. Why he had only one eye is a wonderful story.

Thursday means the Day of Thor. Thor was the God of Thunder and of Battle.

Friday means Friga's Day. Friga was the most beautiful Goddess of Love. Women used to pray to her. These were all English gods. But Saturday means the day of Saturn; and Saturn was a Roman god of time.

CONVERSATION

"My dear little boy, what is your name?"
"Koizumi, Kazuo."
"How old are you now, Kazuo?"
"I am almost eight years old."
"When will be your next birthday?"
"On the seventeenth day of November."
"This is the first of November—is it not?"
"Yes, so my birthday will soon come."
"In sixteen days more. Do you know how many weeks that makes?"
"No."
"How many days make one week?"
"Seven days."
"How many are twice seven?"
"Twice seven are fourteen."
"And two weeks make only fourteen days. But your birthday comes in sixteen days. How many days must you add to fourteen to make sixteen?"
"Two."
"Very well. Fourteen and two days make sixteen: and fourteen days are two weeks. So your birthday will come in two weeks and two days. What day is today?"
"Today is Friday."
"Then your birthday will be on a Sunday."

THE PLANETS

The Sun is a star; but the Earth is a planet. What is a planet?

A planet is a star that has become cold, and turns round a burning star, or sun. Our world was once a burning sun.

There are eight principal planets turning round our sun.

1.———The nearest to the sun is Mercury.
2.———The next is Venus.
3.———Next is our world—the Earth.
4.———Next is Mars.
5.———Next is Jupiter.
6.———Next is Saturn.
7.———Next is Uram[n]us.
8.———Last is Neptune.

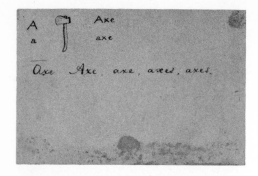

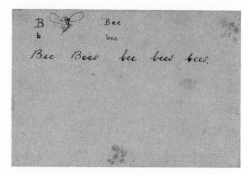

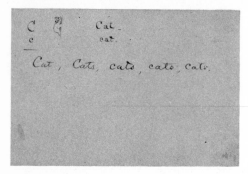

A was an apple-pie. A A A A
B bit it.
B bit the apple-pie, and the lazy boy.
C was a cat. C C C
D was a dog. D D D
D was a dog, and said "Bow-wow!"
D was a dragonfly, with black wings.
E was an egg. E E E
E ate an eel. An egg. An eel.
F was a frog. Brek-kek-kek-kek-ko-ax.
F was a frog;—"Brek-kek-kek-kek-ko-ax!"

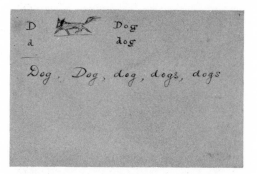

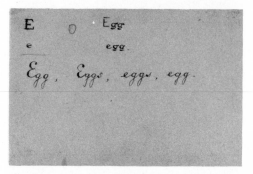

Some of these planets have moons. The Earth has only one moon; but Mars has two moons. Jupiter has four moons. Saturn has eight moons—as well as a ring. Uranus has four moons; and Neptune has one moon.

Between Mars and Jupiter there are nearly two hundred very small worlds called Asteroids.

When Father gave me an alphabet lesson he drew these pictures to explain English words:

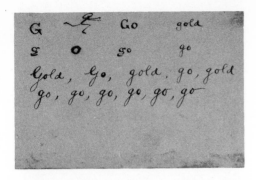

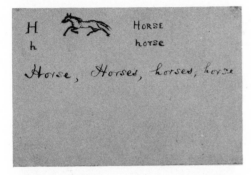

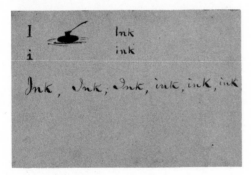

Fly. Frog, fly.
A Frog swallowed a fly.
G was a goat. G G G
G was a goat, with a grey beard.
H was a snow-white horse. H H H
H was a snow-white horse. Horse. H
I am a very nice little boy. I I I
I am now learning how to swim. I I
I am staying at Yaidzu, with my papa.
J was a jelly-fish J J J Jelly-fish
K was a pretty little kitten. K K K
K was a kite—a bird.

K was a kite, a toy.
K kept it. Kept it.
L was a lamp. L L L
L was a little lamb.
L was a ladder. L L L
M was a man. M M M M
the Man in the Moon. M M M
"May I go with you, my pretty Maid?"
M was a small mouse.
N was a newspaper, full of news.
N was a good neighbour. N N
N was a naughty little boy.
N was the name of that boy.
O was an Owl, with big yellow eyes.
O was an Ogre, called Shuten-Dōji.
O was an Ostrich, the tallest of birds.
P was a Peacock, with a beautiful tail.
P P P
P was a Peahen, the Peacock's wife.
P was a Pistol.
Q was a Queen who ate bread and honey.
Q was a queer little monkey.
A duck said:—"Quack, quack!"
Queen, Queen. Queen Q Q Q
R was a Rat that ate malt. R R R
R was a white and black Rabbit.
S was a small Snake. S S S
S was a great Serpent. Snake.
S was a Snail, that carried his house on
his back.
T was a Toad that lived in a pond.
There were many tadpoles in the pond.
T was a Tortoise, or Turtle.
A sea-tortoise is called a Turtle.
U was Urashima Tarō. Urashima.
U was a Unicorn with one horn in his
forehead.
U was an ugly Umbrella.
A silk umbrella. Umbrella.
V was a village called Yaidzu.
V was a viper, a poisonous snake.
V was a flower-vase. Vase.
W was a Wolf with long white teeth.
X was a King called Xerxes.
Y was a Yew-tree. Yourself, Young.
Z was a Zebra—a wild horse striped like
a tiger.

a

A was an apple-pie a a a a a a

A was an apple apple apple-pie pie

apple-"

apple-"

B bit it. B b b b

B bit it. B-B bit it B bit it

a a a

A was an apple...

A was an

Apple apple apple. apple apple apple

apple apple apple

A was an apple-pie A A A

A was an apple-pie A A A

A was an apple-pie

A was an apple-pie

B bit the apple-pie, and the lazy boy

B. bit the apple-pie and the lazy boy

lazy boy

C was a cat C C C C

C was a cat C C C C

D was a dog D D D D D D D

D was a dog

D was a dog, and said "Bow-wow!"

I was a dragonfly, with black wings

I was a dragonfly with black wings

E was an egg. E E E E E E E E E E E

E was an egg. An egg. An eel

E ate an eel. An egg. An egg. An ee

E & ate an eel. An egg. An egg. An ee

A B C D E abcde E E E E E E E E E E

a a A B C D E abcde E E E E E E E E

F was a frog. Brek-kek-kek-kek-ko-a

F F was a frog. 'Brek-kek

F was a frog;—"Brek-kek-kek-kek-ko-ax!"

F F was a frog. "Brek-kek-kek-ko-

Kek.—Koax. Koax!"

A Frog swallowed a fly.
A Frog swallowed a fly.
G was a goat. g g g g g g g g g
g g was a goat. g g g g g g g
g g was a goat g g g g g
G was a goat, with a grey beard.
g g was a goat with a grey
g y; beard;—he ate much paper.
he ate much paper.
H was a snow-white horse. H H
H was a snow-white horse. H H
H H was a snow-white horse.

was a snow-white horse. Horse. A

was a snow-white horse. A

I am a very nice little boy. ♩♩♩♩

I am a very nice little boy

I am now learning how to swim. ♩♩

I am now learning how to swim ♩♩

I am staying at Yaidzu with my papa

I am staying at Yaidzu with

papa papa papa.

was a jelly-fish. ♩♩ jelly-fish. jelly

I was a jelly. ♩ Fi3 hg ♩♩ jelly

was a jelly-fish. jelly-fish.

was at jelly-fish.

was a jelly-fish

J was a jelly-fish. JJJJJJJJ

J was a jelly-fish. JJJJJJ

J was a jelly-fish. jelly JJJJJJ

K K was a pretty little kitten. K K

K K was a pretty little kitten

It was a kite — a bird.

It was a kite, — a find.

It was a kite, — a toy.

It was a kite; — a toy.

It kept it.

It was a lamp.

It was a lamp.

It was a little lamb.

It was a little lamb.

little lamb

L was a ladder.

L was a ladder.

M was a man.   M. M. M.

M was a man.   M. M. M.

the Man in the Moon.   M. M. M.

the Man in the Moon, M. M. M.

"May I go with you, my pretty Maid?"

"May I go with you, my pretty
Maid?"

M was a small House
M was a small Mouse.

N was a Newspaper, full of news.
N was a Newspaper, full of news.

N was a good neighbour. N N

N was a good neighbour. N

N was a naughty little boy.

N was a naughty little boy.

N was the name of that boy.

N was the name of that boy,

O was an Owl, with big yellow eyes

O was an Owl, with big

yellow eyes.

O was an Ogre called Shuten-Dōji.

O was an Ogre called

Shuten-Dōji.

O was an Ostrich, the tallest of

O was an Ostrich, the tallest of

birds. O was an Ostrich,

the tallest of birds.

P was a Peacock, with a beautiful tail. P. P. P. P. P. P. P. P.

P was a Peacock, with a beautiful tail. P. P. P. P.

P was a Peahen, the Peacock's wife.

P was a Peahen, the Peacock's wife.

P was a Pistol.

P was a Pistol.

Q was a Queen who ate bread and honey.

Q was a Queen who ate bread and honey.

Q was a queer little monkey.

Q was a queer little monkey.

A duck said: "Quack, quack, quack!"

A duck said: "Quack, quack!"

It was a Rat that "ate malt. -
R R R was a Rat ate ma
It R R R R R R R R R
R R R R R R R R R R
R R R R R R R R R R
R was a white and black Rabbit
R was a. white and black Rabbit
S was a small snake. S S S S S S
S was a small snake. S S S S S S
S was a great Serpent, snake.
S was a great serpent snake
S was a snail, that carried his house on
his back. S was a snail, that
crawled his house on his back.

was a Toad that lived in a pond.

I was a Toad that lived in a pond.
a pond. There were many tadpoles
in the pond. There were many
tadpoles in the pond.

I was a Tortoise or Turtle.
was a Tortoise.
I was a Tortoise, or Turtle.
A sea-tortoise is called a Turtle.
A sea-tortoise is called a Turtle.

I was Urashima Tarō Urashima
I was Urashima Tarō Urashima

It was a Unicorn with one horn
It was a Unicorn with one horn
in his forehead. It was a Unicorn
with one horn in his
forehead. It was an ugly Umbrella

Umbrella. A silk umbrella. Umbrella.

U was a Village called Yaidzu

I was a village called Yaidzu

V was a viper, a poisonous snake. V

V was a viper, a poison-
ous snake.

V was a flower-vase. Vase

V was a flower-vase. Va-se

W was a Wolf with long white teeth.

W was a Wolf with long whit-
e teeth.

It was a king called Ken

I was a king called

Y was a Yew-tree. Yourself. Young

Y was a Yew-tree. Yourself. Young

Y was a Yew-tree. Yourself.

Y was a
I own

—Za. (It was a Zebra—a wild horse
striped like a tiger.) It was a Zebra—a wild horse
horse striped like a tiger, M.
(& J. J.)

(Yaidzu, August 23rd.
1900.)

Stories Told by Lafcadio Hearn for Kazuo's Copybook

(PREVIOUSLY UNPUBLISHED)

EDITOR'S NOTE

The stories that follow were all given to Kazuo by his father Lafcadio. Kazuo wrote them word for word in his Copybook. From studying the Copybook, it appears that Lafcadio may have written some of the lines which Kazuo copies underneath to improve his penmanship. The excellence of Kazuo's Copybook work compels one to marvel that a ten-year-old boy whose native language was not English could do so well.

Some of these Hearn stories are old favorites retold. But they have a new and charming Hearn quality. Others are inventions or partial inventions by Lafcadio. In each case they are original Hearn dictations, heretofore unpublished. Under each title Kazuo has indicated his recollection of their origin.

THE FISHERMAN AND HIS WIFE

(From Grimm's Fairy Tales — German. Hearn referred to the "Riverside Literature Series," *Fables and Folk Stories*, Part II; but he told the story in his own style. KAZUO.)

Once there was a poor fisherman.
He lived in a little house beside the sea.
He had a wife, but no children.
His wife was selfish; and he was afraid of her.
One day this fisherman caught a very large and beautiful fish.
The fish opened its mouth and said:—"Pray do not kill me. I am not really a fish. I am the Old Man of the Sea."
The kind-hearted fisherman at once let the fish go back to the sea.
Then the fish put its head up, and said:—"Many thanks! If you ever want anything, call me, and I shall come."
But when the fisherman told his wife what had happened, she became very angry, and said:—"You are a great fool! That fish was a god. Go back, and ask him to make us rich."
The fisherman did not like to ask this; but he was afraid of his wife. So he went to the Sea, and called out:—

Once there was a poor fisherman.

Once there was a poor fisherman. (He lived in a little house beside the sea.)

He lived in a little house beside the sea.

He lived in a little house beside the sea. He had a wife, He had a wife, He had a but no children. wife, but no children. His wife was selfish; and he was afraid His wife was selfish; and he was selfish of her. and he was afraid of her.

One day this fisherman caught a very large and beautiful fish.

One day this fisherman cau

a fish. The fish opened its mouth and said:— "Pray do not kill me. The fish opened its mouth and said :— "Pray do not kill me. (I am not really a fish. I am the Old Man of the sea." I am not really of the sea." the Old Man of the sea." I'm not really of the a fish. Ia the Old Man of the sea." The kind-hearted fisherman with The kind-hearted fisherman with at once let the fish go back to the sea at once let the fish go back to the

Then the fish put its head up, and

Then the fish put its head up, an

said:- "Many thanks

said:- "Many thanks! If you

ever want anything, call me, and

ever want any thing, call me,

and I shall come."

I shall come."

(But when the fisherman

But when the fisherman

told his wife what had happened,

told his wife what had happened,

she became very angry, and said:

she became very angry, and said:

"You are a great fool! That

You are a great fool! That

fish was a god. Go back, and

fish was a god. Go back, and

ask him to make us rich."

ask him to make us rich."

The fisherman did not like

The fisherman did not like

to ask this; but he was afraid of

to ask this; but he was afraid of

his wife. So he went to the Sea,

his wife. So he went to the Sea,

and called out :—

out:—

(O Man of the Sea,)

(O Man of the Sea,)

(Come listen to me,)

(Come listen to me,)

(For Alice my wife,)

(For Alice my wife,)

(The plague of my life,)

(The plague of my life,)

(Has sent me to ask a boon of thee,)

(Has sent me to ask a boon of thee!)

thee!

(Then the fish put up its head

Then the fish put up its

head Then the fish put up its

Then the fish put up its head

and asked :- "Well, what does she
and asked :- "Well, what does she
want ?" The fisherman answered:
want ?" The fisherman answered:
"She wants to be rich." The)
"She wants to be rich." The)
fish answered :- "All right! go home
fish answered :- "All right! go home
and you will find her rich."
and you will find her rich."

ts Head,

(The fisherman went home,)

The fisherman went home,

(and found his wife in a most

and found his wife in a most

beautiful house. Before the house

beautiful house. Before the house

there was a beautiful garden. Behind

there was a beautiful garden. Behind

the house there was a storehouse

the house there was a storehouse;

and in the storehouse were twenty

and in the storehouse were twenty

thousand sacks full of gold coin.

thousand sacks full of gold coin.

For a little time the fish-

For a little time the fish-

erman's wife was contented. But

erman's wife was contented. But

after a week she said to her hus-

after a week she said to her hus-

band:—"We are richer than the

band:—"We are richer than the

Bank of Japan; but we have no land

Bank of Japan; but we have no land

Go to the fish, and ask him to

Go to the fish, and ask him to

make you Emperor, and to make me

make you Emperor, and to make me

Empress. The fisherman did not like

Empress.

(to ask this; but he was afraid of
to ask this; but he was afraid of

(his wife. So he went to the sea,
his wife. so he went to the sea,

and cried:—
and cried:—

#—O Man of the Sea,
 " O Man of the Sea,

(Come hither to me,
Come listen to me,
Come hither to me

For Alice my wife,
For Alice my wife,
(The plague of my life,
(The plague of my life,)
Has sent me to beg a boon of thee!
Has set me to beg a boon of thee!

(Then the sea became black
Then the sea became black

and great waves began to roll;
and great waves began to roll;
and the Fish put up its head,
and the Fish put up its head, and
(asked in a terrible voice:—
asked in a terrible voice:—

"What does that woman want?"

"What does that woman want?"

"She wants you to make me

she wants you to make me

Emperor and to make her Empress,"

Emperor and to make her Empress,"

answered the fisherman.

answered the fisherman.

"All right" said the fish,—"go home

"All right," said the fish,—"go home

As the fisherman turned round

As the fisherman turned round

to go home, he saw many soldiers on ho-

to go home, he saw many soldiers on hor-

"O Man of the Sea,
Come listen to me,
For Alice my wife,
The plague of my life,
Has sent me to ask a
      boon of thee!"

Then the fish put up its head, and asked:—"Well, what does she want?" The fisherman answered:—"She wants to be rich." The fish answered:—"All right! Go home, and you will find her rich."

The fisherman went home, and found his wife in a most beautiful house. Before the house there was a beautiful garden. Behind the house there was a storehouse;—and in the storehouse were twenty thousand sacks full of gold coin.

For a little time the fisherman's wife was contented. But after a week she said to her husband:—"We are richer than the Bank of Japan; but we have no rank. Go to the Fish, and ask him to make you Emperor, and to make me Empress."

The fisherman did not like to ask this; but he was afraid of his wife. So he went to the Sea, and cried:—

"O Man of the Sea,
Come hither to me,
Come listen to me,
For Alice my wife,
The plague of my life,
Has sent me to beg a
      boon of thee!"

Then the sea became black, and great waves began to roll; and the Fish put up its head, and asked in a terrible voice:—"What does that woman want?"

"She wants you to make me Emperor and to make her Empress," answered the Fisherman.

"All right," said the Fish,—"go home."

As the Fisherman turned round to go home, he saw many soldiers on horses and a beautiful carriage. The soldiers shouted:—"Hurrah!", and a servant, beautifully dressed, opened the door of the carriage. And the carriage was covered with gold. Then the fisherman got into the carriage; and the carriage took him straight to the palace at Niju-Bashi, the soldiers all riding before him. When he went into the palace he found his wife there dressed like an Empress, with a crown of gold upon her head. And he was Emperor.

For some time the wife was happy. She liked to be Empress, and to live in a palace. But one day she said to her husband:—"It is very nice to be Emperor and Empress. But it is better to be gods. Emperors die, and Empresses die; but gods never die. Go ask the Fish to make us gods."

The Fisherman did not like to do that; but he was afraid of his wife. So he went once more to the sea, and called:—

"O Man of the Sea,
Come listen to me!
For Alice my wife,
The plague of my life,
Has sent me to beg a
      boon of thee!"

Then the sea became green, and great waves rolled and roared, and the fish put up its head, like a mountain, and shouted:—"What do you want?"

"Excuse me!" answered the Fisherman, "we only want to be gods!"

"Go home!" thundered the fish.

And then the fisherman found himself again with his wife in a dirty cottage,—as poor as at first.

THE PIPER OF HAMELIN

(This is a well-known story, but I feel the perfume of Hearn's individuality. KAZUO.)

Hamelin is a little town in Germany. It is a very old town; and it is a very famous town. It is famous because of a strange story about a piper, or flute-player.

Many hundred years ago, there were so many rats in Hamelin that the people did not know what to do. The rats ate up everything, and made noises in the stairs, and in the walls and in the ceilings, and in the floors,—and bit the noses of sleeping babies. So the Mayor of the city promised to give one thousand pieces of gold to anybody who could drive the rats away.

At last a stranger came to the town, and said to the Mayor:—"If I drive all the rats away, will you pay me one thousand pieces of gold?"

"Oh, yes,—certainly," said the Mayor.

Then the stranger went out into the street, and began to play upon a little flute. And at the same moment, there was a noise like the sound of a great rain,—a storm-rain; and hundreds, and thousands, and myriad, and millions of rats ran into the street, and ran after the piper. It was like a great river of rats in the street,—a great grey river. Cats screamed for fear, and climbed up to the roofs;—dogs howled and ran away. But the Piper walked on, and walked on, until he came to the River Weser.

Then he halted on the bank of the river, still playing on his flute. But all the rats jumped into the deep river, and were drowned.

Then the Piper went back to the Mayor, and said:—"Now all the rats are dead. Give me the thousand pieces of gold which you promised."

But the Mayor was not an honest man; and he replied:—"One thousand pieces of gold—that is too much money. Fifty pieces of gold will be quite enough for you, I think."

The Piper said, in an angry voice, "You will not give me the money?"

"I will not," said the Mayor, "only fifty pieces of gold—no more!"

"Then I will play another tune," said the Piper.

"I don't care what tune you play," said the Mayor.

Immediately, the Piper went out into the street, and began to play a strange tune.

And as soon as he began to play, there was a sound of thousands of happy little voices, —and a sound of the pattering of little feet,—and a sound of the clapping of thousands of little hands. And all the little children of the town began to run after the Piper, laughing and jumping for joy. The fathers and the mothers were all afraid; and they wanted to stop the children. But they could not speak—could not call—could not even move.

It was just like a bad dream. In a bad dream you become afraid; but you cannot speak or move. And the Piper walked out of the town—and all the children followed him,—until he came to the foot of a great mountain. And then the side of the mountain opened like a door; and the Piper walked into the hole in the mountain, and all the little children ran in after him. All except one: he was a lame boy, and could not run fast. Then the mountain shut like a door. And neither the Piper nor the children were ever seen again.

THE STORY OF FRANKENSTEIN

(A famous story by Mrs. Shelley, told in Hearn's own style. KAZUO.)

Once there was a young German doctor whose name was Frankenstein. He was very learned. One day he determined to make a living man,—to make a man by chemistry. He said to himself:—"I will make a man finer and stronger and taller and wiser than any other man in the world. I will make a man like a god!"

So he went to work; and he made a man, —a living man,—a man that walked and talked and ate and drank and thought.

But it is not good for any person to try to do the same things that gods do. Only gods really know how to make living men. And Frankenstein made a very bad mistake. He wanted to make a beautiful man, but he was able to make only a frightful monster. The man that he made was taller and stronger and swifter than a real man: but he was so ugly,—so terribly ugly,—that nobody could dare to look at his face. If he went out of the house by daylight, all the people screamed and ran away. So he only went out very late at night, while people slept.

One day he said to Frankenstein:—"You made me. Why did you make me so ugly? It was very wicked to make me so ugly. I cannot live among men. No women can look at me without screaming for fear. But I can go away, and live in deserts, or other lonesome places,—far away from mankind. There I will never cause you any trouble. But I cannot live all alone. You must make a wife for me. Then I shall go."

But Frankenstein sadly made reply:—

"It is true that I did wrong to make you. But if I made a wife for you, that would be still more wicked. For, although you are so ugly, you are stronger than any man, and swifter than any man. And if you had a wife, you would have children stronger than men; and your children, and your children's children would hate men and destroy them. Your children would be all like demons. So I will not make a wife for you."

At these words, the monster became very angry. But he only said to Frankenstein:—"Remember! I will come to your house upon your wedding-night! Upon the night of your marriage I will be revenged!"

Then he went away; and nobody saw him again for five long years.

And Frankenstein almost forgot him. After five years Frankenstein married. The bride was a beautiful girl eighteen years old. Many guests came to the wedding.

At midnight the guests went away; and the bride was left alone for one minute, while Frankenstein was bidding the people good-bye. Then suddenly the monster came in through the window, like a great ape. And like a great ape, he seized the poor bride in his long strong hand; and he tore her limb from limb; he tore her into very small

pieces. And Frankenstein never saw him again. So the monster had his revenge. And poor Frankenstein died of sorrow.

THE STORY OF WILLIAM TELL

(A well-known story, told in Hearn's manner. KAZUO.)

A long time ago there was in Switzerland a man called William Tell. He was a very skillful archer. He was also a brave soldier, and a great patriot. He had one son,—a pretty little boy, seven years old.

One day Tell was seized by the enemies of his country, and taken prisoner. He was then brought before the general of the enemy.

The general of the enemy was called Gessler. He was a very cruel man. He said to Tell:—

"I can kill you; but I do not wish to kill you. I want to see you shoot. People say that you are a very skillful archer. You have a son. I want you to shoot at an apple on your son's head. I shall put the apple on the boy's head; and you must try to hit it at three hundred yards. If you hit it, I will forgive you. If you miss it, I will kill you."

Tell was very unhappy when he heard this. For he knew that if he did not hit the apple, he might kill his little boy. He was not afraid for his own sake. But he had either to shoot or die. It could not be helped.

The soldiers took Tell's little boy, and tied him to a tree, and put an apple on his head. Then Tell was led to a place three hundred yards away and the soldiers gave him a war-bow, and an arrow, and bid him shoot at the apple.

Tell looked at his little son, and hesitated. Then the boy saw that his father was afraid. He cried out:—

"Papa, do not be afraid for my sake! Do not look at my face! Look only at the apple! I am sure that you cannot miss it!"

At these words, Tell's courage came back.

Carefully he took aim, and pulled the bow-string; and the arrow went whistling through the air, and struck the apple right in the middle, and cut in right in two. The little boy was not hurt at all. But the arrow went far into the tree.

Then everybody wondered and shouted; and even the cruel Gessler said, "Well done." But at the same time Gessler saw an arrow in Tell's belt. "Why did you put that arrow in your belt?" he asked. Tell answered:—"If I had killed my son with the first arrow—then I should have killed you with the second."

BLUEBEARD

(From Charles Perrault, but in Hearn's own style. KAZUO.)

Once there was a man called Bluebeard, because his beard was black-blue. This beard made him look so fierce that all women were afraid of him. He was very rich, and lived in a great castle. He wanted a wife; but all the girls were afraid of him. People said that he had formerly had many wives, and that they had all died very suddenly.

But at last Bluebeard found a girl not afraid to marry him. She became his wife; and she took her little sister Anne to Bluebeard's castle.

One day Bluebeard said to her:—

"My dear, I must go on a journey. Here are the keys of all the rooms. You may go into every room except one. Do you see this little key? It is the key of that room. Remember! If you go into that room I will kill you! Don't forget. Now, good-bye!" And he went away.

For a whole month, the young wife and her sister were quite happy in the castle. But one night, while her sister was asleep, the wife took a lamp and went, all alone, to the forbidden room. She wanted so much to see what was inside.

But when she opened the door of that forbidden room, she screamed! The floor of the room was covered with blood; and in that blood were lying the dead bodies of eleven beautiful women. All these had been the wives of Bluebeard. Their heads had been cut off, and lay beside the corpses. It was a horrible sight.

Bluebeard's wife was so frightened that she dropped the key. She picked it up and ran out of the room, and locked the door. At that very moment, she heard her husband's voice, shouting:—

"Wife! bring me the keys!"

She brought the keys, trembling.

He looked first at the key of the forbidden room; and he saw blood upon that key.

"How," he thundered, "did this blood get upon the key? Have you been in the forbidden room?"

She was too much afraid to answer. He drew his sword, and said to her:—

"Now I shall cut off your head! You have been in the forbidden room!"

Then she embraced his knees, and begged him, crying:—

"Oh! let me pray first! let me pray!"

"I will give you just twenty minutes to pray. Go to your room!"

She ran to her room, and awoke her sister.

"Oh! sister, sister! He is going to kill me. Run up to the top of the tower, and tell me if you see anyone coming!"

Then Sister Anne ran up to the top of the tower; and Bluebeard's wife began to pray. For five minutes she prayed. Then she called to her sister:—

"Sister Anne! Sister Anne! Do you see anyone coming?"

Sister Anne made answer:—

"I see only the trees bowing in the wind and the grass waving in the field."

Bluebeard's wife prayed for five minutes more. Then she called again:—

"Sister Anne! Sister Anne! Do you see anyone coming?"

And Sister Anne made answer:—

"I see only the hawks floating in the blue sky, and dust-clouds on the road."

Bluebeard's wife prayed for five minutes more. Then she called again:—

"Sister Anne! Sister Anne! Do you see anyone coming?"

And Sister Anne replied:—

"I see a dust-cloud, coming fast!"

Bluebeard's wife prayed for five minutes more. Bluebeard shouted:—"The twenty minutes are past! Come quick! I must cut your head off!"

But just then two soldiers rushed in and killed Bluebeard.

ABOUT TRYING TO PLEASE PEOPLE

(From Aesop's Fables, but the semi-creation of Hearn. KAZUO.)

An old man and his little son were going to market. The old man rode a donkey. The little boy walked beside the donkey.

People said:—"What a selfish old man! He rides, while the poor little boy has to walk! What a selfish, lazy man!"

When he heard those words, the old man got down from the donkey and put his son on the animal's back.

People said, "What a selfish boy! He rides, and lets his old father walk! What a lazy, selfish boy!"

On hearing these words, the old man got up behind his son, and they both rode on the donkey together.

People said: "What selfish, lazy folk! Two men riding one small donkey. How cruel! How selfish! How lazy!"

On hearing those words, the old man and his son got off the donkey; and the old man said to the boy:—"Let us now carry the donkey and let us hear what people say!"

People wondered to see an old man and a boy carrying a donkey. The donkey's four feet had been tied to a pole; and the old man carried one end of the pole upon his shoulder, and the boy carried the other end.

People said, "What silly folk! What fools to carry a lazy donkey!"

In this world we cannot please everybody. It is no use to try.

ABOUT FOOD

(His creation. KAZUO.)

In Switzerland, very wicked men are sent to prison for life. In the prison these wicked men get only meat to eat, and only wine to drink. The meat and the wine are very good. But the wicked men soon get sick and die. It is very bad to eat only one thing.

THE LITTLE BOY AND THE ORANGE

(His invention. KAZUO.)

There was a little boy who was very fond of oranges. His father told him that he must not eat the seeds of the oranges. But he did not listen to his father; and one day he swallowed a seed. That seed took root in his dear little stomach, and grew up into a little tree; and the branches went into the throat of the boy, and choked him, so that he died.

A ROUGH FRIEND

(I suppose this might be his creation. KAZUO.)

Once there was a man who had a bear-friend. The man and the bear liked each other very much. They hunted together, ate together, and slept together. They never had a quarrel.

One day the man went to sleep in a wood; and the bear sat beside him. Then a fly came, and began to tickle the man's nose. The bear wanted to kill the fly; so he took a big stone, and threw it down upon the fly. The stone crushed and killed the fly; but it also crushed the skull of the man, and killed him.

PAPA'S STORY

(This is his invention. KAZUO.)

In Tokyo there was a little boy named
Koizumi Kazuo. He lived at Number 21
Tomihisachō, in Ushigomé. He was a nice
lad; but he was very much afraid of lions.

One day, when Kazuo's parents were both
out and Kazuo was all alone upstairs, a
strange thing happened—a lion came into
the house. When the lion came in everybody ran away, except Kazuo, who was upstairs. O-Baba San, O-Hana, and O-Yone,
ran to Kobudera, with the baby; Aki ran
to Yotsuya with Iwao; and Niimi ran for
the police.

TWO COOPERS AND A TIGER

(His creation. KAZUO.)

Two coopers were making a very, very
big tub. A tiger suddenly came up behind
them. They were frightened; and they ran
round and round the big tub, and the tiger
ran after them. But, in a little while, they
contrived to turn the tub over the tiger.
It was a very heavy tub, and they sat on
the tub to keep the tiger down. Now there
was a small hole in the bottom of the tub,
and the tail of the tiger came up through
the hole. So they tied a double knot in the
tiger's tail, and ran away. And the tiger
could not run after them, because the knot
in its tail fastened it to the tub.

THE WAY OF THE WORLD

(Perhaps his own invention. KAZUO.)

A pretty butterfly sat upon a bush, drinking dew. A naughty sparrow seized the
butterfly, and ate it. A fierce hawk caught
the sparrow, and devoured it. Just then a
great eagle pounced upon the hawk, and
tore it. At that moment a hunter saw the
eagle, and shot it right through the head.
The eagle fell down dead, and the hunter
went to pick it up. Just then, a tiger sprang

upon the hunter, and killed him, and began
to eat him. Suddenly, a great elephant
rushed at the tiger, and trampled him to
death. In that place there were many
poisonous flies. One of these poisonous flies
got into the right ear of the elephant and
stung him; and the elephant became mad
with pain, and ran about wildly, and fell
over a precipice and was killed.

So this story begins with a fly, and ends
with a fly.

THE SILLY LITTLE BOY

(I suppose this is his own invention. But I remember many years ago I read such a story in some schoolbook. KAZUO.)

I was going down the street yesterday,
and I saw a pretty little boy sitting on the
ground, and crying very loud. I said: "My
dear little boy, why do you cry?" He
sobbed and answered: "Because I have lost
a penny." Then I said: "Is that all? Here
is another penny for you. Do not cry!"
And I gave him a new penny that shone
like gold. He took it, and looked at it, and
began to cry much louder than before. Then
I said: "Why do you cry now? Did I not
give you a penny?" "Yes," he sobbed, "but
if I had not lost that other penny, I should
now have two pennies. That is why I cry!
Boo-hoo-hoo!"

What a silly little boy!

THE JEWEL INSECT

(Perhaps Hearn's creation. KAZUO.)

The Jewel Insect was so pretty that all
the other handsome insects wanted to marry
her. Every day many butterflies and moths
and gnats and other creatures came to her
house, and said to her: "I love you very
much; please be my wife!"

Now the Jewel Insect could not marry
any one of them. But she did not like to
tell them so. She was afraid that they would
get angry with her. So she was cunning

with them, and said to them: "I will marry the first of you who brings me some pretty fire. But remember, it must be really pretty fire, and not cold, like the fire of the fireflies."

They all flew away to get fire for her. But they never came back again. The pretty fire burned them up. And that is why on summer nights, so many insects burn themselves in Mama's lamp.

PRESENCE OF MIND

(Hearn's version of a well-known story from China. KAZUO.)

A long time ago, in China, some little children were playing in the garden of a palace. There was in that garden a very big jar, higher than a man, and it was full of water. The little children amused themselves by climbing up to the top. While playing upon the top, one of them fell in. Some of the children cried; some screamed; but nobody could pull the child out of the jar. The water was too deep. But one boy did not cry or scream. He only took a big stone and broke a big hole in the side of the jar. Then the water ran out, and the child was saved. Presence of mind!

STORY OF A FLOWER

(I believe this is his creation. KAZUO.)

There are strange plants that catch insects and eat them. Some of these queer plants live in water, and some on land.

Some of the plants that live in the water have leaves shaped like little boxes with lids. The little boxes with the lids are really stomachs.

Usually the lids of the little boxes are open in the water. But the moment that a foolish little water-insect goes into one of those tiny boxes, the lid shuts tight; and that little insect never again comes out of the box. What becomes of it?

It melts there, like sugar—all the soft part of it. The hard parts do not melt; and they are afterwards thrown out of the box.

Other plants, which live upon land, have leaves shaped like an open book. Inside there is some sweet sticky stuff, like honey. Little flies come to eat the sweet sticky stuff; and then the leaves shut up, just like a book. And the flies are crushed.

Other plants have long thick leaves like the arms of a cuttlefish. These leaves have sharp thorns inside. When a small animal touches the plant, long arms immediately close and wrap around it; and the long thorns pierce it; and it dies.

These plants eat meat. Now there is a queer story about a man who kept one of these plants in a glass house. I do not say that the story is true; but it is very strange.

There was a man, as I have said, who kept one of these plants in a glass house. Every day he fed it with meat; and every day it became bigger, and ate more and more meat. At last it became a monstrous thing, and every day ate more meat than a hungry lion. All its leaves became like great, long, horrible serpents; and, when anybody came near it, it would stretch out its horrible snakelike leaves, as if asking for food.

Well, one day when the man went to feed the plant, his foot slipped, and he fell upon the plant. Immediately, the horrible plant wrapped its long, snakelike arms around him, just like a great cuttlefish, and began to eat him. He screamed; and his servants came running; and they pulled and pulled in vain. The more they pulled, the faster the plant held its prey.

At last one of the servants took a sharp axe and cut through the roots of the plant with the axe. Then the plant died. But the man was already dead; all his body had been poisoned and crushed by the monstrous plant.

THE LION AND THE MOUSE

(From the Aesop Fables. Hearn's words. KAZUO.)

Once some hunters caught a lion in a net. The net was made of big ropes; and the lion could not break it. He roared and he pulled; but it was no use. Then a little mouse came, and said:—"Be quiet! Do not roar so loud!" And the little mouse gnawed the ropes, and made a hole in the net, and set free the lion.

THE WOLF AND THE STORK

(From the Aesop Fables. Hearn's words. KAZUO.)

Once there was a wolf who was very sick. He was very sick because a little bone had stuck fast in his throat, and he could not get it out. So he asked a stork to help him. The stork put his long bill down the wolf's throat, and pulled out the bone. Some time after, the stork asked the wolf for a favour. "When your head was in my mouth," said the wolf, "I did not bite it off. That was favour enough."

THE THIRSTY CROW

(From the Aesop Fables. Hearn's words. KAZUO.)

Once there was a very thirsty crow. The weather had been so hot that the rivers and ponds had become quite dry.

This crow found a bottle of water. It was a glass bottle; and he saw the water in it; but the water was low down, and the neck of the bottle was very narrow. So the crow could not reach the water with his beak. What do you think he did?

He picked up a great many small stones, and dropped them into the bottle, until the water rose up to the mouth of it.

THE MAN AND THE VIPER

(Also a story from Aesop's Fables. Very brief, but the lucid style is probably Hearn's. KAZUO.)

Once there was a very kind man who loved all living creatures. This good man one morning found a frozen viper by the roadside. "Poor creature!" he said, "how cold you are! But I shall warm you." Thus saying, he put the frozen viper into his bosom, next to his skin. By the warmth of his body the viper soon became revived, and began to move about. The man was very glad; and he put his hand on the viper to stroke it. Then it bit him, and he died. Hence the proverb:—"Never take a viper to your bosom."

THE JACKDAW WITH BORROWED FEATHERS

(From the Aesop Fables. Hearn's words. KAZUO.)

Once there was a very ugly jackdaw. He wished to be beautiful, like a peacock. Where he lived, there were many peacocks; and the peacocks sometimes dropped their feathers. One day the jackdaw thought:— "If I pick up and put on these peacock feathers, I will appear just like a peacock." So he put on a great many peacock feathers, and walked among the peacocks. The peacocks were much astonished to see this stranger. But, after looking at him for a while, they knew that he was only a jackdaw dressed in peacock feathers. They pulled off the feathers, and beat him to death.

THE PINE AND THE BAMBOO

(Hearn's version of one of the Aesop Fables. KAZUO.)

A pine tree and a bamboo grew side by side in a garden. The pine was very old, tall, thick, and strong. The bamboo was young and thin.

The pine said to the young bamboo:— "Oh! you poor, slender, little thing! how weak you are! Don't you wish that you were strong like me?"

Suddenly a great storm-wind began to blow. The pine tree put forth all his strength, to wrestle with the wind. But the wind was a stronger wrestler. The pine tree was thrown down and broken. As for the bamboo, the wind could only bend it to the ground. After the storm, it stood straight up again. It is better to be supple than strong.

THE HUNTERS AND THE BEAR

(A story from the Aesop Fables, but this wording is quite different, and I feel the distinction of Hearn's style. KAZUO.)

Once there were two hunters who went into the woods to kill a bear. As they were walking through the forest, one said to the other:—"The skin of a bear now sells at fifty dollars in the market. So, when we sell the skin, we shall each have twenty-five dollars."

Just as he said those words, a monstrous bear appeared; and the two hunters were so frightened that both of them dropped their guns and ran away. But the bear ran after them. One man climbed a tree.

But the other man could not climb; so he threw himself down upon the ground, and pretended to be dead. For he knew that a bear will not eat a dead body. And when the bear came to the man, it only smelled him and went on without biting him.

When the bear had gone away, the man got up from the ground, and the other hunter came down from the tree. Then the man who had been up the tree said to the other man, for a joke:—"What did the bear whisper into your ear when you were on the ground?" The other answered:—"He whispered only these words, 'First kill the bear; then sell the skin!'"

THE FROG AND THE OX

(From the Aesop Fables. Hearn's words. KAZUO.)

A Frog saw an Ox eating grass in a field. And the Frog became envious of the Ox, because the Ox was so big. And the Frog called a little Frog, and asked:—"Little Frog, am I as big as that Ox?" "Oh, no, no!" said the little Frog. "But I can make my body as large as I please," said the big Frog. "I think you cannot," said the little Frog. Then the big Frog drew a great breath and puffed out her belly like a balloon. "Look!" she said, "am I not as big as the Ox now?"

"Oh, no!" said the little Frog, laughing, "You are not even as big as the foot of the Ox!" Again the big Frog drew a long breath, and puffed out her belly, and asked: —"Am I now as big as the Ox?" "No," answered the little Frog, "you are no bigger now than before." Then the big Frog took another long breath, and puffed out her belly—bigger and bigger and bigger—and suddenly her belly burst with a big bang, and she died—and the little Frog ran away.

THE OLD WOMAN AND THE GOLDEN EGGS

(From the Aesop Fable, "The Goose with the Golden Eggs." Usually the story is about an old man and his goose. Hearn purposely changed it to an old woman and her goose. But I don't know his reason. KAZUO.)

Once there was an old woman. She went one day to market and she bought a goose. It was a wonderful goose. Every day it laid an egg of solid gold.

The old woman took the eggs to market,

to sell them. A merchant gave her one hundred yen for each egg. She was very much surprised.

After that she went every day to market, and sold one egg for a hundred yen. So she got a great deal of money, and became rich.

But she was a miserly old woman. She wanted to become even more rich—quickly. Though the goose laid one gold egg every day, she was not content. She wanted more.

She thought:—"This goose must be made of gold inside, because it lays eggs of gold. So if I kill it and cut it open, I shall get a great deal of gold at once."

So the foolish old woman took the goose and killed it, and cut its belly open to find gold.

But there was no gold. Inside, the goose was just like any other goose.

THE FOX AND THE CROW

(From Aesop's Fables, in Hearn's own style. KAZUO.)

Once a crow went into a kitchen and stole a piece of beef when the cook was not looking. Then the crow flew up into a tree with his beef. A fox saw the crow steal the meat, and determined to cheat the crow. So he went and sat down under the tree and looked up at the crow, and said:—

"Oh! what a beautiful crow! Oh! was there ever in this world before so beautiful a bird? Dear crow, your feathers are black as night and your eyes are bright as stars. What a pity that you have no voice! Alas! alas! you are dumb-dumb-dumb!"

When the crow heard these flattering words, she determined to show that she had a voice; and she said, "Caw! caw! caw!"

But when she opened her beak to cry "Caw!" she let fall the meat; and the fox at once picked it up, and laughed and ran away. Never listen to flattering words.

When your papa was a boy, he was as foolish as this crow. One day he went to

a river to swim. He took off his clothes and dived into the water. Then two boys came to the river bank; and one said "You are very skillful, sir. How far can you dive?" Papa answered, "I think that I can dive across the river." "Please try," said the boy, "we want to see." Then papa dived. He was a long time under the water. When he came up again, he did not see the little boys. Those bad little boys had run away. And they had taken all papa's money, and his watch, and even his penknife. They were thieves, those boys!

THE WOODCUTTER AND THE GOD

(Also from the Aesop Fables, in Hearn's own style. KAZUO.)

Once there was a poor woodcutter who lived in a forest.

One day, when he was cutting a big tree, he let his axe fall in a river that flowed beneath.

Then he sat down and began to cry, for he had no other axe. But suddenly a god rose up from the water, and asked:

"Why do you cry?"

"Because my axe fell into the river," said the man; "and the water is so deep that I cannot get it out."

"Wait," said the god, "I shall try to get it for you." And he dived in.

He was a long time under the water. At last he came up, holding in his hand a beautiful axe that shone like a full moon, and he asked the woodcutter:—

"Is that your axe?"

The man looked at it, and saw that it was made of solid silver.

But he was an honest man, and said, "No, that is not my axe!"

The god immediately dived again, and brought up an axe that shone like the yellow, setting sun. Then he asked the woodcutter:—

"Is that your axe?"

The woodcutter looked at the axe, and

saw that it was made of solid gold. But he was a very honest man; and he said:— "No, that is not my axe!"

A third time the god dived, and soon brought up an ugly, rusty iron axe, and asked:—"Is this your axe?"

"Many, many thanks!" cried the woodcutter. "Indeed, that is my own axe."

The god then said:—

"You are an honest man; so I will now give you the three axes to keep. Always tell the truth!"

So the woodcutter was made very happy. He sold the silver axe and the gold axe for so much money that he became quite rich.

Now, in the same village there was another woodcutter—a bad man. He heard the story of the god and the three axes; and he resolved to deceive the god.

So he went to the river, and let his axe fall in on purpose, and began to cry with a loud voice.

Then the god rose up from the water, with a bright silver axe in his hand. "Is that your axe?" he asked.

The cunning woodcutter thought:— "That is only a silver axe." And he replied, "No."

Then the god brought up an axe of solid gold, and the bad woodcutter shouted:—

"That is my axe!"

And the god cut off his head.

A STORY ABOUT MISTAKES

(Although I do not know the origin of this story, it has the breath of Hearn. KAZUO.)

Once there was a king who was sorry because there were spots upon the face of the Sun. He sent for his wise men—Astrologers and Magicians—and asked them:—

"Can you take away the spots upon the face of the Sun?"

The Astrologers and Magicians said:—

"Yes. The Sun's face is very old;—so it has become dirty. We can clean it."

"How?" asked the King.

"We can rub the Sun, and polish it," said the Astrologers and the Magicians;—"then it will look as good as new."

"But if you make a mistake!" said the King.

"We will not make a mistake," said the Astrologers.

"We cannot make a mistake," said the Magicians.

"Then go and rub the Sun," said the King. "But if you make any mistake, you shall be put into ovens and baked, even as traitors are baked."

Then the Astrologers and Magicians climbed up and began to rub and to scrub the face of the Sun—like a plate. For a long time they rubbed and scrubbed, but the spots remained on the Sun's face. Then they scrubbed again; and many more spots came upon the Sun's face; and the Sun became dim.

So the King was very angry; and he ordered his servants to bake the Astrologers and the Magicians. So they were put into ovens and baked, even as traitors are baked.

But a little time after this happened, other Astrologers and Magicians came to the King, and said:—"Those men that were baked were all fools. They have broken and spoiled the face of the Sun. Please let us mend it."

"How will you mend it?" asked the King.

"We shall rub it with medicine," they answered.

"But if you make a mistake!" said the King.

"Oh, we won't make a mistake!" they said.

"If you make any mistake," said the King, "I shall boil you all alive!"

"We will not make a mistake," they said.

"Now go and mend the Sun," said the King.

So the Astrologers and the Magicians rubbed the face of the Sun with medicine. Then the Sun became very dim, and gave only half the light that it gave before.

So the world became cold. And snow fell;

and the rivers froze; and the King was very angry. Then he told his servants to take those Astrologers and Magicians, and to boil them in pots. So the Astrologers and Magicians were put into pots and boiled alive, even as arch-traitors are boiled.

And always after that, the King sat in his chair before a big fire, rubbing his knees, which were cold, and muttering:—

"Some were baked, and some were boiled!"

TITHONUS

(Hearn's own story. KAZUO.)

Once the beautiful goddess of the dawn, whose name was Aurora, had for her husband a man called Tithonus. It is not good for a man to have a goddess for a wife. Gods and goddesses live forever; men soon die.

Gods and goddesses remain forever young and beautiful; but men and women quickly become ugly and old and weak.

So it is not good for gods and human beings to marry.

But Tithonus was at first a very happy husband. He lived with his wife up in the beautiful blue sky, in the Palace of the Morning, which is all made of white and purple and red and green and yellow and orange clouds.

"Are you very happy?" asked Aurora.

"Yes," Tithonus answered. "But there is one thing which sometimes makes me sad —I remember that I must die. You will never die. Can you not make me live forever? Then I should be quite happy."

When Aurora heard this, she went to the father of all gods, and begged him that Tithonus might live forever. Then the father of the gods gave her a cupful of the Water of Immortality, and said:—"Give this to your husband to drink, and he will never die."

Aurora gave the heavenly drink to her husband; and he drank it, and so became immortal. But he did not become like a god, because Aurora forgot something. She forgot to ask that he should remain always beautiful and young.

So after some years, Tithonus became ugly and weak and old. His head became bald; his beard turned white as snow; his teeth fell out; and his face grew wrinkled like an old dry apple. And he said to his beautiful young wife:—"I want to die! I want to die!"

Then Aurora felt very sorry for him; and she went to the father of the gods, and said:—"My husband wants to die; what shall I do?"

The father of the gods replied:—

"Yes, but he cannot die. He asked to be immortal; and I made him immortal. The gods cannot take back their gifts."

"But can you not make him young again?" asked Aurora.

The father of the gods replied:—

"No. The God of Time would be angry."

Then poor Tithonus became so old that he could not walk, or move, or stand; he became quite blind and deaf; he could not even taste or smell.

He could only lie down, and cry:—"I want to die! I want to die!"

And at last, out of pity, Aurora changed him into a cicada, or *semi*, which cries in trees.

And all day long, in summertime, you can hear Tithonus cry.

THE STORY OF THE GOD THOR

(Hearn's own story. KAZUO.)

One day the god Thor went to the city of the giants. The giants were all as big as mountains; and they laughed at Thor, because he was so little.

The king of the giants said to Thor:—

"At what thing are you skillful? Can you drink?"

"Yes," answered Thor, "I can drink as much as any man alive."

The king said to one of his servants:—

"Give him a cup of ale, and let us see if he can empty it before us."

Then the servant gave Thor a great horn-cup full of ale; and he tried to drink it up. But though he tried very, very hard, he saw that the cup appeared to be as full as before.

Again and again he tried to empty the cup; but all that he could do was to lower the level of the ale in the cup one-tenth of one inch.

Then all the giants laughed; and the king said:—

"Thor, we see that you cannot drink; can you eat?"

"I can eat as much meat as any man," Thor made answer.

"I have a boy-servant who can eat a great deal of meat. Let us see which of you can eat quicker," said the king.

Then a big, long table was covered from end to end with dishes of roast beef; and the little boy sat at one end of the table, and Thor at the other end. "Now," said the king, "let us see which of you can eat quickest."

So they began; and Thor ate very fast. But the little boy ate much faster. And Thor ate only the meat; but the little boy ate the bones and the meat and the plates and the knives and the forks and the table cloth and the table.

"So you can neither eat," said the king. "Then what can you do, Thor? You have no strength."

Thor said, very angry; "Now I defy you to wrestle with me, for I am angry!"

"No, I will not wrestle with you—I do not wrestle with babies. But there is an old grandmother who will very quickly wrestle with you. Come, grandmother!" called the king.

Then an old, old, old, old, woman hobbled into the room, and took hold of Thor, and threw him down. He jumped up, very angry, and seized the old woman and tried to throw her.

But she was much stronger than he; and she threw him again so hard that he could not wrestle any more. And all the giants laughed at him. So he went away ashamed.

But as he was walking all by himself along the road, feeling very sad, the king of the giants overtook him, and said: —

"Brave Thor, you are sad; but you must not be sad. It was all a joke. We deceived you by magic. Listen!

"When we gave you that cup, we really gave you the whole sea to drink. Even a god cannot drink up the sea. But you drank so much, Thor, that the sea has gone back three miles from shore.

"Then you could not eat as fast as our boy-servant. But the real name of that little boy is Fire! Men also call him the Hungry Ghost.

"Then the old, old woman threw you down; and you felt ashamed. But the name of that woman is Old Age; and even the gods cannot overcome Old Age."

THE DRAGON'S HEART

(Probably Hearn's own creation. He lectured me w i t h o u t looking at a book. KAZUO.)

Once there was a brave warrior called Sigurd. He was the strongest man in the whole world.

In the time when Sigurd lived, there were big dragons in the country. They breathed fire; and they flew about on their big wings, and spat fire and poison on the fields, and killed a great many people.

One of these dragons was killed by Sigurd.

After having killed the dragon, Sigurd was very tired and hungry. He cut out the dragon's heart, and made a fire, and cooked it. When it had been well roasted, he tasted it. Then a strange thing happened. He heard the birds singing; and he knew what they said. He understood the language of birds. And the birds were singing these words:—

"Sigurd's enemy is waiting to kill him; Sigurd's enemy is hiding in the bushes behind him."

Then Sigurd looked around and saw that enemy, and cut off his head.

So he saved his own life.

If you want to know the language of birds, you must eat the heart of a dragon. Also, let me tell you this secret—

You can always catch a bird if you can put a little salt on his tail.

But you must not throw the salt. You must lay it very gently on the bird's tail; then you can catch the bird. It is a very hard thing to do.

Try!

THE SIRENS

(Well-known story, as told by Hearn. KAZUO.)

The Greeks used to tell strange stories about three monsters called the Sirens. These Sirens had faces like beautiful girls, and voices sweeter than birds. But their bodies were like the bodies of monstrous eagles; and they had claws of brass.

And they used to sit by the shore of the sea, hiding their bodies and showing only their beautiful faces,—and singing. And when any man heard them sing, he had to go to them—could not help going to them.

And, as soon as he came close to them, the Sirens caught him with their brazen claws, and tore him, and devoured him. And the shore where they sat and sang was white with old bones of men.

There was one very skillful captain called Ulysses. When his ship had to sail by the shore, he stuffed the ears of his sailors with wax so that they could not hear the Sirens. And he made the sailors tie his own body to the mast so that he could not move. Then the ship sailed on, and soon the sailors could see the beautiful faces of the Sirens. But they could not hear them sing; so nobody jumped into the sea. Ulysses himself could hear them; and he wanted very much to jump into the sea and swim to them. But he could not jump into the sea, because he was tied fast to the ship.

THE STORY OF ICARUS

(An old story, told in Hearn's own manner. KAZUO.)

Icarus was the son of a man named Daedalus. Daedalus was the most skillful carpenter in the world. One day his little son wanted to fly; so Daedalus made him wings.

These wings were made of wax and feathers.

Daedalus then said to his son:—

"My dear boy, you can fly with these wings. But you must not fly too high with them; for if you go near the sun, the wax will melt, and you will fall down and be killed."

Then Icarus put on the wonderful wings which his father had made; and he said good-bye to his parents, and flew away over the roofs of the town. He flew higher and higher into the sky; then he saw the bright blue sea, and he thought, "I will fly over the sea!"

And he began to fly over the sea. He was now so high above it that he could not see the waves at all; it was just like a great blue looking-glass. But suddenly Icarus gave a terrible scream.

One of his wings had come off, because the sun had melted the wax. He fell into the sea, and was drowned.

ORPHEUS AND EURYDICE

(Well-known Greek myth, told in Hearn's own way. KAZUO.)

Once, in Greece, there was a man called Orpheus. When he played upon his harp, the trees bowed down their heads to hear. When he played upon his harp, the fishes put their heads out of the water to listen, and lions and tigers came to lick his feet, and birds and frogs and snakes wept for joy.

When he walked along a road, playing on his harp, the woods moved after him, and even the rocks followed him. He was the best musician in the world, because the gods taught him the harp.

But the most wonderful music that he ever played was not in the world, but in the World of the Dead.

For his dear young wife Eurydice was bitten by a poisonous serpent, and died; and Orpheus went after her to the black World of the Dead, and made music before the King of the Dead, until the King of the Dead shed tears of iron.

And the King of Death said, while the iron tears rolled down his cheeks:—

"Orpheus, I will give you back your wife. When you return, she will follow you. But you must not turn your head to look at her until you are out of the black World of the Dead. If you do, she will be taken away from you again."

Then Orpheus thanked the King of the Dead, and went away from that dim world. And behind walked Eurydice, silently as a shadow. And Orpheus did not hear the sound of her feet, but only the sound of her breathing.

And he wished so much to see her face again that he could not wait until he had passed the Gate of the Dead. He turned; he saw her; he called, "Eurydice." But Eurydice answered only with a bitter cry. In the same moment, two long black arms stretched out of the dark behind her and snatched her away forever.

THE STORY OF KING MIDAS

(An old story, told in Hearn's own manner. KAZUO.)

Once, in Greece, there was a king called Midas, who had ears like an ass. The reason that he had ears like an ass was this:—

One day, the God of the Sun and the God of the Forest both played the flute before King Midas; and they asked King Midas to tell them which played best; and Midas said that the Forest God was more skillful than the Sun God. Then the Sun God became very angry, and said to Midas, "Because you do not know good music from bad, I shall give you the ears of an ass." And immediately the ears of the poor king were changed to the ears of an ass.

King Midas was very much ashamed of his ears. So he had a cap made to hide those long, ugly, hairy ears.

But sometimes King Midas had to get a barber to cut his hair and to trim his beard; and, at such times, he had to take off the cap, and the barber then saw the long, ugly, hairy ears.

The barber was forbidden to tell anybody that the King had ass's ears. But it was very hard for him to keep the secret. So he dug a hole in a field, and whispered into the hole: "King Midas has ass's ears!" Then he filled up the hole with earth, and went away happy. But, soon afterwards, some reeds grew up in that place; and, when the wind blew, those reeds whispered:—"King Midas has ass's ears!"

KING SOLOMON WAS A VERY WISE KING

(I believe this story is Hearn's own invention. KAZUO.)

Once King Solomon was visited by an angel from heaven. The angel held in his hand a beautiful diamond cup, full of water that shone like moonlight.

And the angel said to King Solomon:—

"In this cup I bring you some water from the Fountain of Life. If you drink this water you will never die, and you will remain forever young and strong. Therefore, drink and praise God."

But Solomon asked:—"Can I share this gift with others?"

"No," said the angel; "it is forbidden."

King Solomon said:—"Then, before I
drink, I wish to speak to all living creatures
and ask for their advice." And he sent mes-
sengers to all men, animals, and birds.

Then all living creatures came before
King Solomon; and he told them about the
Water of Life, and asked them whether they
wished that he should drink it.

"Drink, and live forever, O King!"

"Have all creatures spoken?" he asked.

"Only the wild dove has not spoken, O
King," they said.

So Solomon questioned the wild dove;
and the wild dove said to him:—

"Do you wish to live forever, O King
—when all who love you are dead,—when
all whom you love are dead,—when the
eyes that watched for your coming are dust,
—when all the voices that you liked to hear
are silent? How could you wish to live
then? Even the wild dove will die if its
mate dies!"

When Solomon heard those words, he gave
back the cup to the angel.

UNDINE

(On old legend. KAZUO.)

A long time ago, people believed that
there were spirits or ghosts of Earth and
Air and Water and Fire. The spirits of
Earth were called Gnomes; they lived under
the ground. The spirits of Air were called
Sylphs. The spirits of Fire were called Sala-
manders. And the spirits of Water were
called Undines.

There was a man once who wanted to
marry an Undine. The Undine was very
pretty and very gentle. She said to him:—
"If I marry you, you must be very kind to
me, or you will die. I am not a woman,
but a water-fairy; and if you are ever unkind to me, my relations, the water-people,
will kill you."

The man wanted very much to marry
the Undine; and he promised to be very
kind. Then he married her; and for six
months he kept his promise. But, after that
time, he became selfish, and went away and
married another woman.

Then strange things happened. If he went
near the seashore, great waves would rise
up and rush roaring over the beach in pursuit of him. If he crossed a river, horrible
faces would appear in the water. If he
passed over a bridge, long black hands would
reach up from the water and try to catch
his feet. And, in his own house, the water
of the well overflowed, roaring; and ghosts
came up with the water. Then he had an
enormous stone put over the mouth of the
well; and he got priests to write a holy
charm on the stone.

But the second wife was very angry because the well had been closed. She said
that her husband was a fool to be afraid
of ghosts; and she wanted some of that
water to wash her beautiful face; and she
made her servants take away the stone.

On the night after the stone had been
taken away, the water in the well rose up
very high; and with it rose up the white
form of a woman. And the white woman
ascended the stairs, without any sound, and
passed into the room of the sleeping man
and took him in her arms, and said:—

"Now you must die. My relations, the
water-people, will kill you, if I do not: so
it is better that I should kill you."

Then she kissed him, and wept, and her
tears flowed like a river; and with her tears
she drowned her ungrateful husband.

Around Home---In Japan

EXCERPTS FROM THE COPYBOOKS

Father taught me the alphabet and grammar. After I had learned to write English, I kept a diary. I was ten years old when I wrote the following in my Copybook:

Yesterday we gathered plums from the tree in the garden. We got a basket and a ladder, and a bamboo pole. There were many plums in the tree. I put the ladder against the tree, and climbed up, and plucked all the plums that I could reach. I could not reach some of the plums, so as to pluck them; they were too high up. But I was able to knock them down with the bamboo pole. We filled the basket quite full of plums; and we had plenty of fun.

Last year Papa brought home, from the University, some English clover, and planted it in the garden. It grew and spread, and this year it blossomed very nicely. Next year, perhaps, it will spread much more. The flowers of the clover have a sweet smell; and bees are very fond of them because they contain honey, or[,] rather, nectar.

Now Shiro has four puppies. One is white-and-black; another is brown and white; another is reddish-brown and black and white; and the fourth is all black. I like the all black pup the best. Now Shiro barks at all people; for she thinks the people will take away the puppies.

Today I translated a song about a proud girl. She was walking in the wood early in the morning; and she saw a bird sitting on a bush, and she asked the bird, "When shall I marry?" Then the bird answered: "When six fine gentlemen carry you to the church." Then she asked the bird again, "Who will make the bridal bed?" And the bird replies: "The gray-haired sexton will make the bed." And the bird said again:—"And the glow-worm will give you light, over the graves and gravestones; and the owl will cry to you, 'Welcome, proud lady.'"

Last night the snow fell; and this morning the trees were white with snow. In the garden the snow was deep; and the bamboos were bending under the weight of the snow. I played with the snow; I made nine snowballs, and I painted them like cakes. Then I made a target of paper, and threw snowballs at it.

Iwao caught cold yesterday; and this morning he stayed in bed, and I played with him. We played war-ships on the blankets. Our ships were made of paper; Iwao's paper ships were the Japanese fleet, and mine were the Russian fleet,—and Iwao won.

Today I was in the garden playing with a hoop; and I stumbled as I was running, and fell and I made my hands very dirty. Then Papa called me. Then Papa saw my dirty hands, and said, "Where have you been? Go and wash your hands."

Today I was very naughty and disobedient[,] and so my father set me to taking dictation as follows:—

"Can you write Japanese?" "Only a little." "Can you write a Japanese letter as well as Nakumura? (a rikisha-man)" "No, I cannot." "Can you read a Japanese newspaper?" "No." "Can you read a Japanese letter?" "No." "Can you write or read or speak English well?" "No." "Have you learned any trade?" "No." "When papa is dead, how will you make some money?" "I do not know." "If you do not know, this house will be taken and sold—you will have no home—and your mamma and grandmamma will be dead—and you will have no friend. Then you will find how cruel people are in this world."

Today Mama is sick; and the house is very lonesome. The weather is cold, and snow is falling;—and therefore it is still more lonesome. We play very quietly, because mamma is sick. I wish to please mamma—to cheer her up. I think that I shall tell her the story of the Twelve Brothers.

Today Mamma is quite well. Today papa went to the University; and while papa was away, I translated into Japanese the poem called, "Boy Johnny." The poem was very easy to translate; but the name Johnny, was very hard to spell.

Today I have a cough; and mamma also. I have no appetite, and[,] at dinner time[,] I ate only two oranges. Today I am not so strong as usual. Therefore today papa will let me off the French lesson. But papa will not let me off the arithmetic lesson.

Now the season of spring is beginning. The clover in the garden was changed from brown to green; and the little plum-trees are blossoming. This morning I heard the nightingale sing—that is a sign of spring.

Today we have very fine weather; but a cold wind is blowing. Early this morning there was frost—a white frost. In the garden a little plum-tree is now blossoming; and the flowers are bright red, and the buds are pink. Soon the frogs will begin to sing.

Today, Wednesday the 23rd of March, Papa went to the University; and while papa was out I translated into Japanese the poem about the "wind" in "A Child's Garden of Verses." It was very easy, and I translated it very quickly.

Today is a real spring day. This morning, in the garden[,] I heard a wasp humming.

I made a sand-glass with two bottles[,] but it is not quite finished yet. I think that I will soon finish it; but the sand in the garden is coarse[,] so I must make the hole big. I wish I could get some fine sand.

Today the sky is grey and dark, and the weather is damp and cold;—so we cannot play in the garden. This morning we amused ourselves in the house. We played at fishing. We made nooses; and we tried who could put both hands at the same time into a noose, without getting caught. We called the noose a net; our hands were the fishes.

Since early this morning it has been raining and it is chilly and dark. This morning there was no fire in papa's room, because the stove had to be cleaned; and papa, to keep himself warm, went to bed. Papa said, "[I]n England there is a proverb—March comes in like a lion, and goes out like a lamb." But this year, in Japan, March came in like a lamb, and is now going out like a lion.

Today is very fine weather; but the wind is blowing very hard and it is roaring through the trees. This morning I was on the swing; and the wind whistled in my ears, so that I could not hear anything else. The wind makes all the bamboos bow down before it.

Today is very fine weather; and Iwao and Kyoshi and I practiced gymnastics, and made a sand-hill. This morning papa went to the University;—while papa was out, I translated into Japanese the poem entitled "A Good Play," from the book called: "A Child's Garden of Verses." It is not difficult to translate.

This morning the weather was cloudy; but in the afternoon the sun shone for a little while. We played in the garden and practiced gymnastics. Today the sand is wet[,] because it rained last night. We went to the post-office, to deposit some money in the post-office savings bank. We all save money every month, and put it in the postal savings-bank.

Papa says that my hand-writing is shameful.

This morning the weather was cloudy; but in the afternoon the sun began to shine. After dinner the director of the neighbouring school came to teach me. He gave me a lesson in reading for one hour, and he said that I remembered the Japanese characters rather well.

Today the weather is warm and fine; and the cherry-trees are budding. Today Papa went to the University; and while papa was away, I translated into Japanese the poem called, "My Bed is a Boat."

It has been raining all day; but this morning I heard the nightingale sing. We cannot go into the garden; so we play indoors. Now the plum flowers are falling and it is very sad to see them fall. But the cherry-trees will soon be in flower.

Today Papa went to the University; and while he was away, I translated into Japanese the poem entitled "The Moon"—from "A Child's Garden of Verses." It was very easy. This afternoon there is a great wind, which is scattering the petals of the plum-flowers over the garden—so that the ground seems as if covered with snow.

Now the cherry-trees are all blossoming. Today is a very hot day; and the sand in the garden almost burns one's feet. The peach-trees also are beginning to bloom.

There were three little birds in a nest. The nest was on the roof, very high up;—the parent-birds had built it where the cat could not get at it. "Take care not to fall out of the nest," said the parent birds; "—if you fall out, something horrible will happen to you." But the little birds did not listen to this advice. One day, while quarreling, they fell out of the nest, and a big ugly dog ate them up.

We put a little sparrow in a cage. It was too young to fly, or to feed itself. But its mother came every day to the cage, to feed it. Sometimes she fed it with insects:—sometimes she fed it with crumbs of bread which she found in the garden. The baby-sparrow would open its little yellow bill;—then the mother would poke the food into its mouth. How pretty to watch the mother-love of a little bird!

It has been raining all day. This morning I went to school, and I took my lunch with me. As it was raining, we had to play in the schoolroom.

Today in school we had lessons in reading and writing and mental arithmetic. We had also a lesson in gymnastics. In the school-grounds now there is a flower-bed; and our teacher will teach us the names of the plants, and will give us some lessons in botany. All the boys and girls are going to present plants or seeds to the teacher for the garden.

Yesterday, at school, we had lessons in reading, writing and literary composition. The teacher wrote a little story on the blackboard, with chalk; and then we all wrote the same story on our slates—each in his own way. The story was about Nara, in the time when Nara was the capital of Japan, more than eleven hundred years ago.[1]

Today is a very windy day;—perhaps there will be a storm, or a typhoon. The sky is dark; but the thermometer stands at seventy-five degrees, and the air feels heavy. "The wind is roaring in turret and tree."

Today the gardener is rooting up the bamboo-grass, there is too much bamboo-grass. Its roots grow very deep, and to remove them, one must dig far down.

This afternoon a newspaper "extra" announced a Japanese victory in Korea. Yesterday the soldiers who had been staying in Okubo, went away to the war; and we all went to see them off. All the people sang war-songs. Before all the houses[,] little flags were put up. The soldiers were artillery men; they had many horses and waggons. In the waggons I saw many rice sacks and rice-pots. I saw many cartridge-boxes. When you were a soldier, did you wear a sword?

Yes, I wore a sword.

The Japanese warriors used to be called samurai;—they were allowed to wear two swords.

Today is a holiday,—the holiday called

---

[1] The capital of Japan was in Nara from A.D. 709 to A.D. 784.

Shokonsha; so the school closed early, early, early. Today all the soldiers are in full-dress uniform.

"To beleaguer" — to surround a place with soldiers. "Vague" — dim, not clearly seen. "Host" — an army. "Spectre" — a ghost. "Marvellous" — wonderful. "Legend" — an old story.

In my school there are many different kinds of boys; and there is one boy who is full of insatiable curiosity—like the *Elephant's Child*.

He asks all kinds of questions—as, "Where did you buy that cap? Where did your mother buy her umbrella? How much did it cost?" Some of his questions are bad; but some of his questions are good.

Now in the school-grounds we have a flower bed; and yesterday all the pupils made a railing around it. The teacher taught us how to make the railing;—perhaps it would be better to call it a wire fence. We planted little posts in the ground, and fixed wires from post to post, twisting the wires round the posts, or passing the wires through holes in the wood.

Today is the festival of our Shintō parish-temple; and drums are being beaten and children are dancing. So[,] this morning[,] the school closed sooner than usual.

Yesterday, at school, we played at "the tug-of-war." We were divided into two parties,—one was called the Genji, and one was called the Heike. I was with the Genji; and we won four times.

This morning the teacher announced that tomorrow will be a half-holiday, because tomorrow there will be a Shintō parish-temple festival in the neighbouring district. The day after tomorrow also will be a holiday; and the day after the day after tomorrow will be Sunday.

This afternoon Papa called me into the garden; a queer caterpillar was crawling over the stepping-stones, and he wanted me to see it. It was very hairy, and of different colours, and it moved very fast. In our garden there are many extraordinary caterpillars,—some are so strange that even to see them makes you afraid.

The Director of the school gave me a new arithmetic the other day. The author of the arithmetic is Mr. Sakutarō Inagaki. It is very easy to remember the name, for my brother Iwao's name is Inagaki. Papa says that my writing is very careless.

The school-holidays begin t o m o r r o w. Yesterday the teacher gave me three books. Two of them are reading books; and one of them is a writing book. In the reading books there are pictures and stories. In the writing book there are Chinese characters. I am to copy the characters on paper.

I have been today very selfish, and have caused mamma much pain. I have quarreled, and struck my little brother[,] and made everybody in the house unhappy. Yet mamma loves me so much that she does not want papa to punish me. She loves me too much—and I have been very bad, very unkind, and very selfish. But I am very sorry, and I will try to be good from today, and to please mamma.

Today is very hot, and the thermometer stands at ninety degrees. Now the sunflower plants have ten flowers and three buds. The big aloe-plants have now become very strong; but one aloe plant seems to be very feeble; its leaves get smaller every year, instead of bigger.

Dear Papa took me to Yaidzu on the tenth day of this month. We stayed there nineteen days,—swimming, diving, eating, drinking, sleeping, boating, fishing, catching dragonflies and crabs and grasshoppers. We all got sunburnt—especially Iwao. He became as brown as any Yaidzu boy; and some Yaidzu boys are so brown they seem to be black.

The five senses are (1) Sight, (2) Hearing, (3) Smell, (4) Taste, and (5) Touch. The word "sense[,]" in the singular[,] also means intelligence—natural power to understand. Intelligence, or common sense, is very different from the knowledge that we get from books.

Suzuko is my baby sister. She is eleven months old; and she is very tender and small and plump. Though she is so young, she likes to laugh and crow and play. When she laughs[,] she jumps up and down, and waves her little hands. She cannot talk yet; but she can say "Bo," "Ah, bah," and "Ah."

Now the weather is very hot; and today I heard the tsuku-tsuku-bōshi. When that cicada begins to cry, we know that the autumn is near. The butterflies are flying about the flowers; some of the butterflies are yellow; some are velvety black; some are white as snow. The sunflower plant has three buds.

On the window there is a very curious moth. It has horns like feathers. By the horns we know that it is a moth—not a butterfly. Butterflies have horns shaped like clubs. Moths have horns of different shapes.

Today I saw many lizards—I think there must have been at least ten. They were basking on the ground, in the bamboo-grove. They were of beautiful changing colours;—when they moved the colours changed. Sometimes they appeared to be purple, sometimes red, sometimes green, sometimes brown like the ground, and sometimes black.

Now the cicadas are crying with all their might, because the autumn has come, and they will not have much longer to sing.

Soon there will be frost; and when the frost comes, they will all die. Now the crape-myrtle, which the Japanese call *sarusuberi,* is blossoming.

(End of Kazuo's Diary)

THE POSTMEN

One of Father's fantastic drawings is in his old notebook. He arranged many postmen running in a row towards him from afar, like the Marathon race. The volcano might be Fuji, symbol of Japan. Father wrote:

The sun is rising and the ship is entering, come, come, come every postman to hand me the mail from my dear western friends, or the proof-sheets from the American publisher, for which I've longed so much, for more than a month.

In Father's day, the mail steamer used to take several weeks for one voyage. At the top of the picture he wrote: "In the sight of him to whom a million years are but a moment." And, beside the tree, there is written in Japanese characters, *Doko* ("Where?"). And, on the right side, *Yubin koi-koi!* ("Come, come, mails!"). And two other postmen are running on the top of the paper, one of them carrying a big envelope. Beside them, on the edge of the leaf, there are three eccentric designs.

While Father was in Japan, he was afraid of calls by the foreign guests, especially the missionaries, because at this time there were many "phony" missionaries. He did not go to Hakone, nor did he go to Nikko nor Karuizawa, because there were so many foreigners. Thereupon, he was misunderstood as a misanthrope; but I remember that he wanted eagerly to get mail from Western

friends, and every day he asked us, "Are there any letters for me?" And when he had some good letters from his friends, he jumped around the room with joy, just like a small child who had gotten some sweets or toys that he wanted.

THE ACTIVE THIN CREATURES

His imaginary sketches I found in his pocket notebook. He demonized these small black thin figures purposely. We cannot guess whether these small, devilish creatures are nail men or needle men or pin men. But these figures are, and look, very active in their paper world—danc-

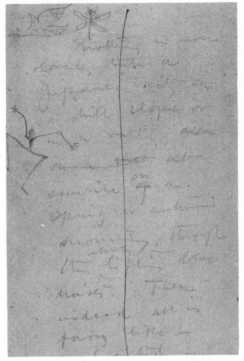

ing, running, quarreling, jumping, and trooping. Do you suppose the dancing figures are Papa dancing when letters from Western friends arrived in Japan?

If they are nails, we can imagine such words as follow: hard as nails, right as nails, be off (or go off) at the nail, clench nail, French nail, drive a nail (or add a nail) in one's coffin, go at it tooth and nail, hit the nail on the head, nails in mourning, to the nail, fasten with nails, nail a lie, nail a bad coin to the counter, nail down, nail up, nailed-up drama, nail one's colours to the mast, and so forth.

And if they are needles, we can

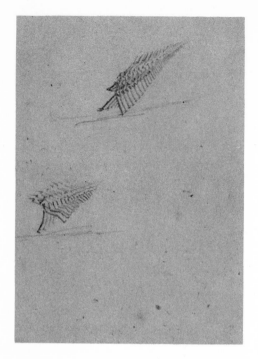

The boy's face which is looking with amazement at these active figures might be my face in childhood —*Kazuo-bō*. (Kazuo-bo; *bo* means "a little one.")

And written underneath the dragonfly are Father's words:

Nothing is more lovely than a Japanese city on a hill slope or in a valley, seen at sunrise on a spring or autumn morning, through the slowly lifting blue mist. Then indeed all is fairylike—enchanted.

MANY EXPRESSIONS

These faces are collected from Father's several notebooks. Most of them are pictures from his imagination. But a few of them are his depictions of real people.

Father discusses faces:

. . . Faces are not *read*. The impressions they give are only *felt*, and have much of the same vague character as impressions of sound—making within us mental states either pleasant or unpleasant or somewhat of both—evoking now a sense of danger, now a melting sympathy, occasionally a gentle sadness.[2]

A and B might be the faces of his friends from which he took the person's likeness. C, the cabbage-like face looks like an imaginary depiction. D, E, and F are the faces of the Yaidzu fishermen. H and I look like the demons' faces of a Buddhist

conceive these words: get the needle, have the pin and needle, look for a needle in a bundle of hay, needle in a bottle of hay, he is sharp as a needle, and so forth.

And, if they are pins, we can associate them with the next words: be on one's pins, in a merry pin, not worth a pin, pin-fire cartridge, sit on pins, he is quick on his pins, I don't care a pin, there is not a pin to choose between, you might have heard a pin fall, pin one down to, pin one's faith upon another's sleeve, and so forth.

See a pin and pick it up,
    All the day you'll have good luck;
See a pin and let it lay,
    Bad luck you'll have all the day!

[2] Lafcadio Hearn, *Exotics and Retrospectives* (Boston: Little, Brown and Company, 1910), p. 191.

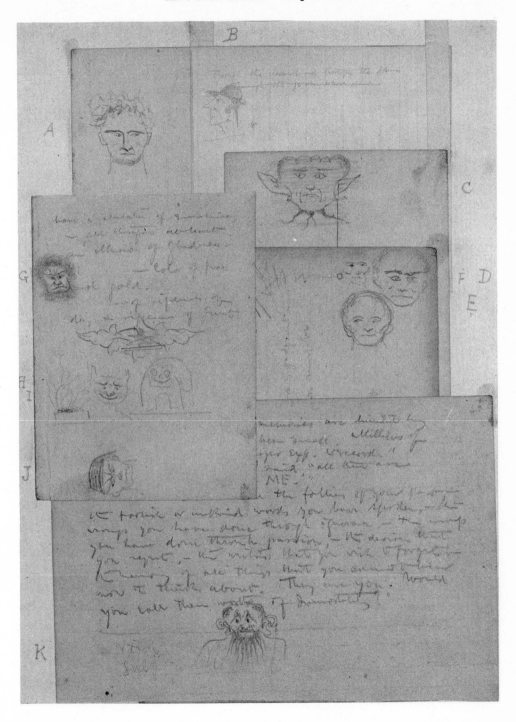

temple. This is from his old pocket notebook where he had notes about some Buddhist temples and Shinto shrines.

G and J, the two fearful faces, are drawn on the same page as H and I. I couldn't guess what kind of men's faces they are. But I remember he told us that he saw two very fearful men's faces in Japan. One was at Nagasaki or Yokohama (I don't remember distinctly). Anyhow, it was in a port town, and the man was a stout Chinese crew member. The other evil face he saw at some station while the trains passed. It was a middle-aged Japanese man who cast a murderous, malevolent

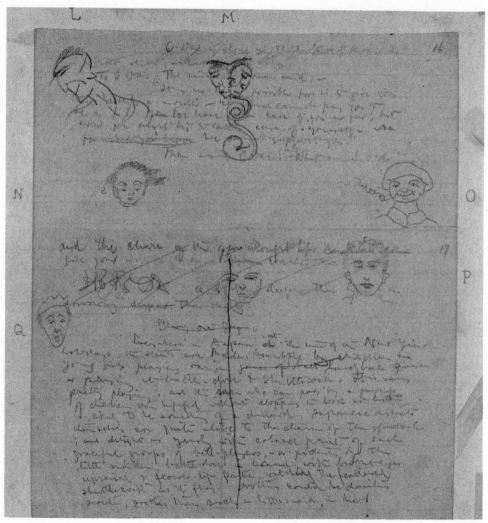

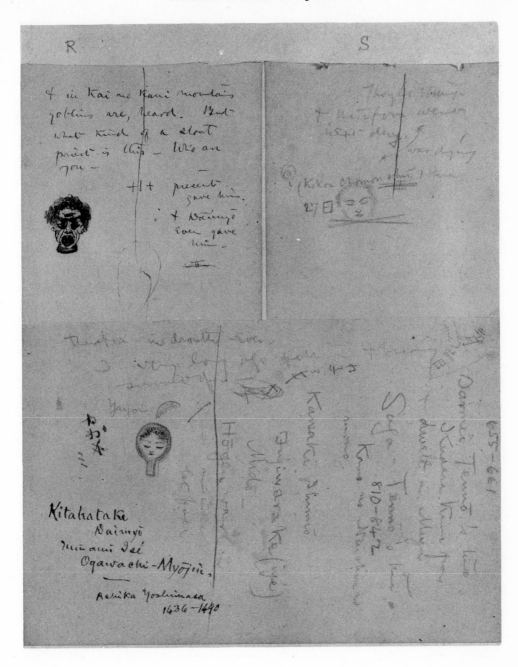

glance from the window of the opposite car. Perhaps these faces are his memory of the two men.

K is an imaginary picture. It looks like some old Chinese scholar or a diviner. L, M, N, O, P, and Q are miniatures from his imagination, drawn in ennui, I suppose.

R is the demon of the *Rokurokubi*. He drew this on the memo of *Rokuro-kubi*, the goblin of Whirling Neck, or Rotating Neck, which appeared in his book *Kwaidan*.

S—at the end of the note on the tradition *Oshidori* ("mandarin ducks"), he had drawn this woman's face. The story of *Oshidori* is also published in *Kwaidan*.

T is from the note on "The Mirror Maiden," which is a story from his book *The Romance of the Milky Way*.

WE BROTHERS

My father drew these pictures of my brother and me when we were about the same age. But of course they weren't drawn at the same time. I was six years old (1899)

and Iwao was s e v e n years old (1904).

When Father gave us our lessons, I was always a crybaby, but my younger brother Iwao was a boy easily given to laughter. Father blamed me and said, "Are you a mosquito?" or "Hurry up, you snailboy!" And Iwao was scolded with, "What a rude boy you are. There is nothing for laughter."

In my Copybook I wrote:

I am a relation of the snail; and my pen moves much more slowly than a snail.

DEAR PAPA:—

I do not like to study: I like to play much better than to study—all little boys dislike study. So I was very angry when you called me. But I know that I was wrong, and that I must study in order to become a wise and good man, and to help mamma. So please forgive

Your naughty little son,
KAZUO

May 10, 1903

NIPPON-NO-ONNA
and
KODOMO

On the right side of a woman's face he wrote, in Japanese characters, *Nippon-no-Onna,* or "a Japanese woman;" and, beside the child's face, *Kodomo,* or "child." She looks like a chambermaid in the Meiji-era and her face looks like some of

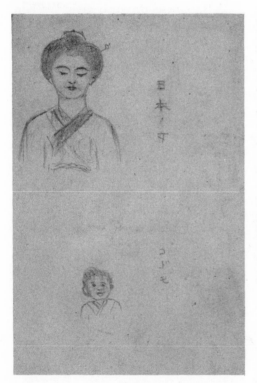

the faces in Buddhistic statues. The child might be a country boy. They are not my mother and I.

SKETCHES OF MOUNT FUJI

This picture (the black Mount Fuji) was found in his investigative notebook of *The Romance of the Milky Way,* and there is no relation between his memo and the sketch of Mount Fuji. Beside Fuji, here again we can find the queer design-like faces—which is his usual trick.

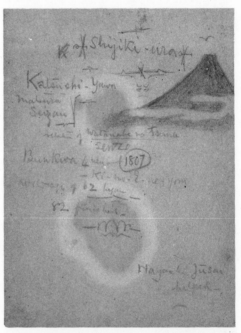

The other sketch of Mount Fuji was in the same pocket notebook in which he made the sketch of the view "Rockies and the Mountain Gates." This little notebook was a farewell gift from his friends, Mr. and Mrs. Rollins, before his voyage to Japan in March, 1890. So it is possible that this view of Mount Fuji was sketched by him from the deck of the Canadian Pacific vessel SS *Abyssinia*.

What do you think of the picture of a bird on the mountain of Fuji? The bird stretches its wings wide. It looks like the mark of the American colonel's shoulder sign. Is it an eagle or a pigeon or a crow? Most people say that it is a raven, for it was drawn by black pencil and my father's nickname was A Raven. There is even a book, a collection of his letters, called *Letters from the Raven*. But I guess that this picture might be a hawk. Because in Japan there is a word of interpretation for dreams: "Best is the Mt. Fuji, better is the hawk, good is the eggplant." In this picture we can easily find Mount Fuji and the hawk; but where is the eggplant? Please look at someone's nose. . . .

The two snails looking at each other are not going to attack, though their poses resemble the bullfighter. But their weapons are too soft and mild for a quarrel. They are going to salute each other. Their horns are their eyes. But they are not so fearful as the telescopes of the submarine. My father, who had only one eye, was always envying this four-eyed creature, and he loved it. I remember he called me, "Come on, be quick, my snail!" And once he told me about the dainty dish of the fried, edible snails which he had tasted when he was in America.

A Japanese proverb says, "Where there is a will, there is a way." Even the snail can climb to the top of Mount Fuji if it has the will.

The bundle-like i m a g e under Mount Fuji may be a sheaf. Almost all the writing in the picture was the memo of his story of Itō Norisuké in the book *The Romance of the Milky Way*. They have nothing to do with these drawings.

But the word *I-no-toshi-no-Aki* means "The Autumn of the *Year of the Boar*." The year of my father's birth was 1850, and it falls in the boar year. The Japanese say that the man who is born in boar year has the character of a headlong rush. His word *Aki*, "the Autumn," means no mere autumn season. It seems to suggest the explanation of the autumn of his life. When Father was teaching me, he was in the autumn of his life. He would always say to hurry up and learn because Papa's life could not wait. And now, to think of it makes me sad.

BAKÉ JIZŌ

This goblinish, smiling face appeared in his old, small, pocket notebook. It is a monk with an eerie look—but he is not a human being; he is a kind of stone Buddha. He is a Baké-Jizō, the goblin Jizō. Perhaps Father drew this while he made the translation of "Goblin Poetry." If you see my father's "Goblin Poetry" in his book *The Romance of the Milky Way, and Other Studies*

and Stories, you will find a poem as follows:

> NANIGE NAKI
> ISHI NO JIZŌ NO
> SUGATA SAÉ
> YO WA OSOROSHIKI
> MIKAGÉ TOZO NARU

Although the stone Jizō looks as if nothing were the matter with it, they say that at night it assumes an awful aspect; or, although this image appears to be a common stone Jizō, they say that at night it becomes an awful Jizō of granite. The Japanese word for granite is *mikagé*. And there is also a term of honor—*mikage*, applied to divinities and emperors, which signifies "august aspect," "sacred reading." *Kagé* signifies "shadow," "aspect," and "power" . . . especially occult power. The honorific prefix *mi* attached to names and attributes of divinities may be rendered "august."

The Jizo is the Deity of Mercy, and Father said:

The figure of the Bodhi-sattva Jizo, the savior of children's ghosts, is one of the most beautiful and humane in Japanese Budhism. Statues of this divinity may be seen in almost every village and by every roadside. But some statues of Jizo are said to do uncanny things—such as walk about at night in various disguises. A statue of this kind is called Baké-Jizō,[3] meaning a Jizō that undergoes transformation. A conventional picture shows a little boy about to place the customary child's-offering of rice-cakes before the stone image of Jizō, —not suspecting that the statue moves, and is slowly bending down toward him.

---

[3] Perhaps the term might be rendered "Shape-changing Jizo." The verb *bakéru* means "to change shape," "to undergo metamorphosis," "to haunt," and many other supernatural things.

The moonrise and the **Torii**. Here is the same kind of illusion which Hearn admired.

TORII

Torii, the shrine entrances, were drawn in his old pocket notebook. He wrote about the Torii in his book *Glimpses of Unfamiliar Japan*.

. . . The first time you see a noble one, you will imagine, perhaps, that you see the colossal model of some beautiful Chinese letter towering against the sky; for all the lines of the thing have the grace of an animated ideograph,—have the bold angles and curves of characters made with four sweeps of a master-brush.

The Torii stands against the big rising moon and its long, ghostlike shadow stretches mystically for miles. Father was fond of such a phenomenon, and he often drew views like this. (The picture of a steamboat with wheels is the sketch of a toy of my childhood. It is neither a tank nor a landing boat.)

Two Torii beside the seashore. This might be an imaginary picture; but there are many such views in Japan.

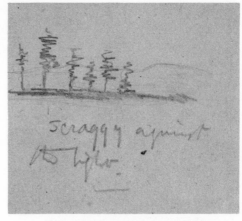

Shinto shrines in the area of Izumo

SCRAGGY AGAINST THE HEIGHT

This is a very simple scratch sketch I found in Father's old memorandum. His words, "scraggy against the height," make me delight to look at this rough sketch. His brief words and quick picture imply some philosophical meanings.

HEARN'S ROOMS AT OTOKITCHI'S UPSTAIRS (1902)

Off to the Seashore--- Yaidzu!

At Yaidzu, the seaside place where my father loved to go in the summer, he would write a letter to my mother every day. She usually stayed at home in Tokyo because she did not like to remain long at the seaside place. But she joined us when summer vacation was almost over. Father never wrote her a letter which was not illustrated by his own pictures of frogs, snakes, snails, insects, birds, cats, mice, fish, fishermen, boats, boys' faces, and landscapes.

These sketches (see page 145) were drawn by Father during his stay at Yaidzu, and most of them were in his letters to Mother, in Tokyo.

THE SNAILS

LITTLE LOVELY MAMA:

Weather is beyond description. Kazuo studies well. Nothing is amiss.

August fifth, Yaidzu

from PAPA

Snail says: "Lovely weather, indeed."
Frog says: "Amusing weather."
Duck says: "Quack, quack."

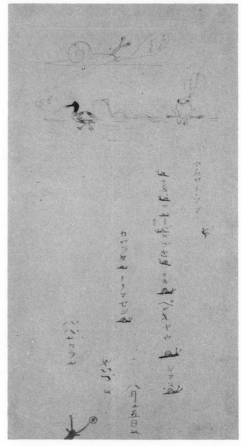

[Look at the head of the largest snail at the bottom. The one-eyed snail is the symbol of Papa.]

THE FUJI, CRAB, AND MICE

In the letter of August 20, 1904, he wrote, "Fuji was seen clearly last evening," and he illustrated this sketch of the scenery of Fuji.

And he wrote, "Iwao let his crabs walk on the roofs of Otokichi's house; and they walked and walked." By this, he drew the picture of a crab, and wrote beside it in Japanese character, O-ko-sekai, or "the world of a side-crawler." The word O-ko-sekai we can roughly classify into three divisions, "Oh, this (my) world," "the world of going side-wise," and "the world of rampancy." Ō means "Oh"; kō means "this"; and sekai means "world."

He drew the pictures of four mice gathering in towards a wire-made soapbox and he wrote: "During the night the mice tried to bite into the

box of our soap, but it was beyond their power to open the wire cover."

When we went to Yaidzu, we stayed with the Otokichi family. They were a nice family. The food was good and we had the upper rooms which overlooked the sea. We had an upstairs living room, with a picture window the length of the entire room. Sometimes at night Papa would tell us all stories. And he learned Japanese well enough for the Otokichis to understand.

THE THREE SMALL SKETCHES

These three small pictures are illustrations in letters from Yaidzu, too. At Yaidzu, Father laid aside his individuality and became like any ordinary person, wearing yukata ("summer dress") all day, and going out in Zōri ("straw sandals"). Everyone addressed him as Sensei ("Professor"). He jumped naked into the sea, and walked a great deal. He often walked to the shrine of Yamatodake-no-mikoto, which was surrounded by great rice stalks. We frequently went to where the black dragonflies p l a y e d around Ogawa-no-Jizō, near a small stream, or along the breakwaters, welcomed by the waves, passing along the pine avenue; through reed-grown swamps by narrow paths where red crabs played in numbers. We would

stop at Wada peninsula and rest at the teahouse of a woman who had lost her son in the sea, and drink lemonade.

The sketch of the insects are those which we caught on the way to Wada.

It was his taste to draw such a view as a boat sailing in front of the rising sun. He frequently drew such a view—some figure standing, or walking, or running, or sailing, or flying in front of the rising sun, or setting sun, or rising moon, or setting moon.

The picture of the frog says *Arigato Kami-sama,* or "T h a n k God." One day, at Yaidzu, we were caught in a shower at the seashore, and we hurried back to our lodging. While we were changing our wet clothes in our upstairs room, we heard a quacking voice of an *ama-gaeru* or a rain frog, a green frog living upon a tree or bush, that cries with joy when it rains. He was calling from the neighbor's banana tree in their back yard. That day, when my father wrote his daily letter home, he illustrated it with this picture.

THE GHOST SHIP

Sailors say that there is a ghost ship. This ship is called "The Flying Dutchman." It is not like any ship of today; it is like a Dutch ship of three hundred years ago. It sails very, very fast, and is seen only in the times of great storms. And it is bad luck to see that ship. To see it is an omen of death; and when

The View of Yaidzu Bay (1900)

The View of Yaidzu Bay
(1901)

The View of Yaidzu Bay (1902)

The view of Yaidzu Bay, but in the opposite direction from the former views. It is in the direction of Wada Province (1904)

A VIEW OF YAIDZU FROM THE BACK WINDOW OF OTOKICHI'S UPSTAIRS, LEFT SIDE, THE OAK TREE IN THE EVENING GLOW (1904)

"Is it that the trees have been so long domesticated and caressed by man in this land of the Gods, that they have acquired souls, and strive to show their gratitude, like women loved, by making themselves more beautiful for man's sake?"

FROM *Glimpses of Unfamiliar Japan*
By LAFCADIO HEARN

View of Yaidzu from the back window of Otokichi's upstairs, right side, in the morning (1902)

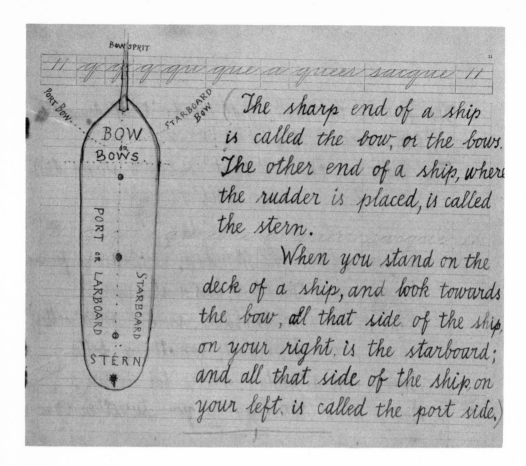

sailors see it, they know that their own ship is going to sink, and that they will be drowned.

And in my Copybook Father drew a diagram of a ship.

The sharp end of a ship is called the bow, or the bows. The other end of a ship, where the rudder is placed, is called the stern.

When you stand on the deck of a ship, and look towards the bow, all that side of the ship, on your right, is the starboard; and all that side of the ship, on your left, is the port side.

THE SINGED RICE FIELD

This is a sketch at Yaidzu. One evening, while we brothers and playmates were painting some pictures about some interesting events of that day, Father came and looked at our painting. He sat down beside us, took up a paint brush, and painted this picture (see page 148), which was the view from one of the village shrines where we had gone that morning. Usually, when he drew pictures, he would use pen or pencil, even when he was using water colors. But, for this picture, he used only a painting brush, like a pure Japanese painter. While he was painting, he dropped his brush by accident, and it made a black spot on the left side of the picture plane. But pretty soon he changed this black spot to a dark shower-cloud, because we had had a shower just that noon. Can you find the black spot under the clouds?

This picture was completed very quickly. Father took only a few minutes, as the Japanese painters do. Father held it over the hanging oil lamp to dry. But, this time, it ended in complete failure. The lower part of this picture, the rice field of Yaidzu village, was singed. Do you see where the oil lamp burned the picture?

HINOKO AT THE SEASHORE

Japanese cats are most fond of fishes, especially the bonitos. There is a Japanese proverb, *"Neko ni Katsuwo-bushi no ban wo saseru."* This means, "To set the cat to keep the dried bonito"—equal to the Western proverb, "To set the fox to keep the geese." But the fish in this picture are not dried bonitos. They are fresh, raw bonitos.

One day we carried our cat Hinoko (or "Spark") to the seashore with us. Just at that time a fishing

boat came back with a heavy hand of bonitos, and there was a great hubbub on the beach; the young pussy Hinoko was staring at them, eyes like live coals, in astonishment.

The next day Father drew this picture in his letter to Mother. Hinoko says: *"Dō-shi-yō,"* or "What shall I do?"

THE SINGED RICE FIELDS

THE MOONRISE

THE CATS

Father was so fond of cats that he always kept some cats while he lived or stayed in New Orleans, Saint Pierre, Matsue, Tokyo, and Yaidzu. I heard that in the West Indies he kept many cats to guard against the bad creatures—the centipedes, serpents, poisonous snakes, and vermin.

The face of the black cat might have been drawn when Father was in the French West Indies. I found this sketch in the old memo he used at Saint Pierre.

The other picture was found in a small pocket notebook which he used as a memo at the University of Tokyo.

A STUDY IN THE CAR

After beginning my English lessons, Father never stopped a single day, except when one of us was ill. But, for a slight cold or stomach-ache, we never rested. Even New

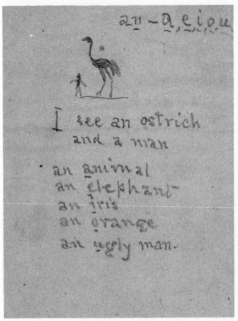

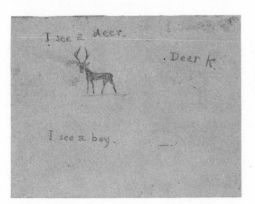

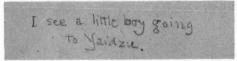

Year's, Sundays, and holidays, it was just the same. "Learn q u i c k l y , please; time won't wait; papa's life will not wait," he said frequently.

When he took me to Yaidzu, the

summer of 1899, he gave me a brief English study in the running railway car. He took out a pencil and pocket notebook and drew these pictures, and wrote down these words for me to read and answer, although everything was quaking and very noisy in the car.

THE STORY OF THE SPIDER

(Hearn's version of a Greek myth. KAZUO.)

Long ago there was a girl called Arachne. Arachne used to weave very skillfully; she was the best weaver in the whole world. But she was proud.

In the village were several temples . . . and, near the house where the girl lived, there was a temple of the Goddess of Weaving. All the other girls of the village prayed to the goddess, and made gifts to the temple. But the girl Arachne never went to the temple. And, one day, she said that she was able to weave even better than the Goddess of Weavers.

At that very moment, the goddess herself came into the room, bright like the moon, and said:—"Can you really weave better than I?" Then Arachne was afraid and ashamed, and could not say a word. And the goddess struck her with a shuttle, saying:—"Weave forever! spin forever!" And poor Arachne was immediately changed into a spider. Now she lives in dark corners only, and weaves thin webs to catch flies.

THE BLIND MEN AND THE ELEPHANT

(This is his creation, but he got a hint from an old Chinese proverb, "Gun-mō Zō wo hyōsu," "A crowd of blind criticise an elephant." KAZUO.)

One day four blind men went to feel a great elephant. One felt a leg of the elephant, and said:—

"The elephant is like a big pillar."

Another felt only the trunk of the elephant. He said:—

"The elephant is like a big serpent."

Another felt only the side of the elephant, and said:—

"The elephant is like a wall."

Another felt only the tusk of the elephant, and said:—

"The elephant is like a stake."

All were mistaken;—nevertheless they told the truth.

+ is the Sign of Addition

× is the Sign of Multiplication

− is the Sign of Subtraction

÷ is the Sign of Division

MY ARITHMETIC STUDY

When Father taught me arithmetic for the symbol of subtraction he often drew many such pictures as of the Yaidzu fishermen who were landing their boats. And for the symbol of division he drew a crab who was the owner of a pair of shears, or with a sword he divided the head of a man.

THE LUNAR MYSTERY

. . . . Breaking open the heavens to their highest, night widens modern thought over the bounds of life and death by the spectacle of the Infinite whose veil is day. . . .[1]

On the sky, my father's eye would often be transfixed.

. . . A full moon looks into my study over the trees of the temple-garden, and brings me the recollection of a little Buddhist poem:

> "From the foot of the mountain, many are the paths ascending in shadow; but from the cloudless summit all who climb behold the self-same moon."[2]

These three mystic pictures of the moon are reproduced from Father's "Goblin Poetry," which I compiled and which was published by Oyama, Tokyo, Japan, in 1934.

Father was never a lunarian, but he was very fond of moonlight and, on clear nights, he was in the habit of staying awake 'til late at night, looking at the moon. He was a one-eyed man as I said before, but not moon-eyed. He was a moon lover.

You will notice two bats in his moon pictures. They recall to my mind a story Papa made up for my Copybook lesson.

[1] Lafcadio Hearn, *Exotics and Retrospectives* (Boston: Little, Brown and Company, 1910), p. 212.
[2] *Ibid.*, p. 153.

ABOUT A BAT

Once a cat, whose name was Tama, caught a bat. "Oh! let me go! let me go!" "Why should I let you go?" asked the cat: "It is my duty to kill rats and mice." "But I am neither a rat nor a mouse," said the bat; "I am a bird." "You look very much like a mouse," said Tama; "but perhaps you are really a bird. You have fur like a mouse, and ears like a mouse. But you have wings, and you can fly, though your wings are so queer—you look like an umbrella. But perhaps you are a bird; and I am not hungry now. So I will let you go."

"A thousand thanks!" said the bat, and flew away in great joy. But, as it was flying, an eagle caught it, and fiercely held it fast. "Oh! let me go! let me go!" said the bat. "Why should I let you go? It is my duty to kill birds. If I did not kill them, there would be too many birds in the world." "But I am not a bird," said the bat; "I am only a poor little mouse." "I thought you were a bird," said the eagle, "because I saw you flying about. But you have fur like a mouse. You are not a bird—perhaps you are the ghost of an umbrella. Good-bye!" And he let the bat go.

What a clever bat!

THE MOONRISE

One summer evening we all went to the shore at Yaidzu — father, mother, brother, pupil, servants, Otokichi the gay fishmonger, and I—to have a bath in the sea. We took hands all in a row and went into the cool water singing merrily; when the waves came, we jumped over them with shrieking, shouting, and laughing. And we had a very pleasant time. Soon after, we noticed that the far-off sky of the horizon became gleaming, and a big, round, yellow-bright moon began to rise. Its ghostly, pale light shone over and through the ripples, glittering and throwing an ivorylike, queer lustre upon our faces and bodies. And after a few minutes, unexpectedly, a long, black, sashlike cloud appeared, and extended a line over the surface of the mirrored moon. Father greatly admired this view, and the next day he painted this picture. (See page 148.)

In clear, cloudless weather at Yaidzu, when we looked towards the sea, we could see Mount Fuji to the left; but, in this picture, Father painted it on the right. So we cannot say that this is an exact sketch of Yaidzu Bay. This might be some other place which Father knew, or a creation of his fancy.

Kazuo---On Father's Art

Father was never quite able, within himself, to compose his Western roots with his new and deep love for things of the Orient. He loved Japan, but he continued to love Martinique of the West Indies, and the warm, enchanted, dreamlike city of Saint Pierre, and even the serpent-like city of New Orleans. He wrote to some friends, "Still I love it so much. I love New Orleans."

I believe it was Father's great love for the simple things, liked by all people everywhere, which gave the universal appeal to his works. He loved small animals, birds, insects, and fishes. He loved the dog, cat, mouse, weasel, sparrow, swallow, *uguisu* ("Japanese nightingale"), *yamabato* ("Japanese turtle dove"), owl, crow, kite, duck, snake, frog, lizard, snail, beetle, ant, bee, butterfly, dragonfly, firefly, cicada, cricket, spider, tortoise, goldfish, carp, and he was never unkind even to the caterpillar, fly, or mosquito.

Also, Father loved plants. He was fond of Japanese flowers, and he planted many of them in his garden. But he was also fond of Western flowers, and he planted them, too—especially roses.

Although Father was neither a professional artist nor a poet, he had some techniques of both. One biographer has written that, when Father was a reporter in New Orleans, he filled his notebook with sketches as well as notes. I am sure this might have happened.

It is difficult for me to say to what school of art he belonged. But the style of his pictures is Western—rather more romantic than realistic. And they contain some impressionistic tendency to Celtic humor, and a touch of queer, exotic, Oriental ghostliness.

My father had only one good eye, and it was myopic; but he was never a one-eyed, evil man. His was a life of light and shade. This trait is clearly reflected in all his sketches. Even his caricatures of "The Postmen," "The Owl," "The Moonrise," and the "Torii," reflect exaggerated shadowings. He loved the summer-like warmth and the bright, luminous colours. But, on the other hand, he never forgot to be fond of the cool shades or the faint, gloomy shadows.

It has been frequently said that "Hearn's portraits always show only the right side, to hide his blind eye." And some cynic has said, "He looked only at the right side of the world." And then another criticized, "He wrote a one-sided view of Japan so that the reader knew Japan only as a lovely, pretty, mystical, interesting country—a land of the sun with no shadows." But, in his letters, Father did not hesitate to disclose his sharp criticisms and deep grievances.

This I can explain. He was delighted with Japanese art, the touching folklore, the delicate customs of flower arrangement, the miniature, gardenlike, lovely landscapes, and the sweet, melodious, singing insects. He introduced these charming things and deeds of Japan to foreign countries openly, through his published works. This was *his* Japan—exotic, dreamy, beautiful, free from shadows.

But Father was unhappy about bureaucratic Japan. He became disillusioned with the Japanese family system. He saw the awful abuses of power, and the government's con-tempt for the people on every level throughout Japan. In letters to intimate friends he complained about these unfortunate matters. He saw, quite clearly, the deepening shadows forecasting tragedy and doom.

Father's books were open to all, but his letters were private. His books are like the outward appearance of a man who puts on a newly cleaned and well-folded outdoor suit, so that his appearance is without shadow and irreproachable.

But the letters which are written to friends are as the form of a man who is at home, who throws himself into an easy chair, clothed in only a shirt, open wide so that even the hair on his chest appears. And thus he unburdens himself to talk frankly without reserve to friends of many years standing. So, sometimes, father's letters are rather rough, and seem to cast dark shadows.

I am not a student of the arts. I cannot define my father's painting scholastically. But, in a general sense, I can say that the Occidental pictures are painted with much account of shadowings, though the Oriental pictures are unshadowed and most heedful to the linear effects.

I think that my father made a remarkable analysis of Japanese art. He grasped the essential difference between Western and Eastern art.

Japanese art, he felt, "produces sensations of Nature no Western picture could give . . . the inexplicable color is Nature's own. But why does the thing seem so ghostly? . . . Chiefly because of the absence of shadows."

The Japanese, Father discovered, "had no admiration for the shadows that blacken and break the charm of the world under the sun. . . ." Psychologically, also, the Japanese "saw life without shadows."

Then Father explained how the impact of the West on Japan introduced "shadows of machinery and chimneys and telegraph poles . . . and factories . . . and houses twenty stories high. . . ."

Japan tried to shake off these shadows, but the Japanese "could not possibly get rid of them. Never again could the world seem quite so beautiful as it did before."

And how Father would have been stunned and hurt by the great, towering, black shadows caused by these awful, futile wars—the East against the West.

On War's Futility

During World War II I was afraid that Father's treasured manuscripts would be burned in an incendiary bomb attack. I divided his mementos into three packages, two of which I left with friends. I kept one packet. One package my friend stored in a warehouse which was burned; the other package was stolen.

In RE-ECHO, all of Father's remaining unpublished original work will have been published. The few manuscripts and sketches which I now possess are as the cast-off skins of the cicadas or snakes, although they are quaint and dear to me.

Almost every day during World War II I wrote poems—not for publication but for consolation. When the stupid war was over and I observed that nearly all the men of the Allied Occupation were gentlemen, I dug out of our back yard our household goods and the package into which I had put a portion of my father's books, drawings, old notebooks, and manuscripts.

As I aired them out in the sun-beams, under the bright, blue, peaceful, autumn sky in which there were no more air raids, the memories of the dear old days of my childhood returned into my heart. If some publisher would reproduce Hearn's drawings, there might be many people who would have an interest in them.

In the beginning of the Pacific war, I read in the newspapers that a new American ship was being built, and that the authorities planned to name it "Lafcadio Hearn." Against this plan a whirlwind-like counter-blast was hurled, and a multitude of letters of opposition piled up on the office desks of American authorities. Most of the nation had the opinion that "Lafcadio Hearn was a noted writer in the United States and Japan but he was married to a Japanese woman and he was naturalized in Japan, and his sons might be fighting the United States. It is imprudent to name our ship for such a man."

I had been greatly inspired by

the proposal to name an American ship for my father, Lafcadio Hearn. And I felt grateful to the authorities who made the proposal. But, at the same time, I felt a reverence for the patriotism of the United States. These same antagonists who objected to naming the ship for my father have led the United States to a great victory. And we, Hearn's family, have reason to be thankful to them. If the ship had been named "Lafcadio Hearn," we, H e a r n ' s family, would have been treated like spies by the *Kempei* ("gendarmerie" or "policemen").

My father died about forty years before the beginning of the Pacific war. His sons were too old or too nearsighted to go to the front. Only one of his grandsons (my only son) was called. He served as a radio operator. His transport was attacked by an American submarine seventy-five miles northeast of Palaoa on the twenty-ninth of February (leap year day). My nineteen-year-old boy was wounded on the left leg; but, fortunately, he was helped. He was picked up by a Japanese torpedo boat named *Sagi* or *The Heron;* quite a coincidence, because Father had used the heron for his crest.

During the war a famous English gentleman coined a phrase to show to the world his determination. I don't know if it was a quotation or an accidental agreement, but his words resembled my father's words in his book *Kottō* in a sentence of "A Drop of Dew" ". . . drops of dew and rain and sap, of blood and sweat and tears. . . ." Whether it was a quotation or not, I could entertain good will toward him.

American bombers that were shot down would sometimes yield men who would come down by parachute and lurk in the rice fields where they were taken captive. Many villagers, each carrying a bamboo spear, would surround the fugitive. A young Japanese countryman who took part in such an affair told me about it.

From the position of the parachute, they imagined that the rice field might be the American's hiding place. Under the direction of policemen, the villagers went into the field to find him. My friend had his heart in his boots. Suddenly a huge fellow stood up just in front of my friend.

The American lifted his hands up so high that he seemed an even greater giant than at first. Probably he meant to surrender by holding up his hands, but my friend was startled and jumped to the conclusion that the American was going to attack him. So my friend immediately prepared his bamboo spear and shouted with all his might, *"Itá, itá!"* which means "Here he is!" But the giant was only holding up his hands to surrender, and he was not going to strike at my friend.

In spite of his tremendous size, with a gentle, soft tone he said something in a foreign tongue. My friend could not understand the meaning. Policemen came rushing across the rice field and, surrounded by many people, the American who came down from the sky was taken to prison. He went in a gentle, obedient manner.

Although the American was a man of gigantic frame, he might have been a young lad of about twenty years, because his blue eyes, blond hair and apple-like cheeks, his soft, childish voice, and all his looks seemed quite young. At about the same time, in the next village, two other birdmen were captured.

The mother of my friend said that she had seen the prisoners of war peeping out from behind the crowd when they passed her street in the convoy to the prison. She noticed the giant, blond American. And she thought he might be about the same age as her other son who was a student in Naval Pilot Training School (*Kami-kazé*). She began to be anxious and said: "I don't think it possible, but if he should be taken captive as that young man. . . . Oh, God!"

"He would sooner die than disgrace himself. We are Japanese," my friend forced himself to say boldly.

"Just as you say," she replied. But her eyes filled with tears. After a little while she suddenly exclaimed: "How horrible the war is!" And she sighed. My friend was of the same sentiment, but here again he put on a bold face and said:

"It is no use talking with such a weak will. Aren't you the mother of an Imperial soldier? Japan must continue this war until we are triumphant."

But my friend knew very well that the odds were against us. He also understood his mother's feeling. But it was very queer. He felt it his duty to speak boldly. And, like a man possessed, he whistled a war song and went to the barn, where he wept secretly.

It weighed heavily on the mind of my f r i e n d about the young prisoner of war—perhaps because the Americans neither bombed nor burned my friend's village. But, even so, my friend could not hate the young, big, blond boy from the bottom of his heart. But he could not let anyone know this. He felt as if he had another soul besides his regular one. This other soul acted upon him powerfully and forced him to say or do something which was different from what he felt in his heart.

Some Japanese ladies went to inquire after the health of the prisoners of war in Tokyo. One of them uttered a word of sympathy, "*O-kawaiso.*" The word "O" has no meaning. It is usually used to honor or show politeness; *kawaiso* means poor, pitiable, miserable, or wretched. The lady's word, *O-kawaiso*, came into question. Simultaneously all the Japanese papers cast blame upon her word. Principals in schools blamed her, too, brandishing their hands or striking their desks, shouting and roaring before their boys and girls. Some reporters said that her words of pity were unpatriotic.

To feel pity is a characteristic of womanhood. Japanese women were hereditarily educated in such a way. In former war times, the Japanese military never interfered in the woman's world; neither in the Sino-Japanese War nor the Russo-Japanese War. But, in the recent war, the military trod on the woman's world too much. The military used women to fight fire. They were pressed upon to ride on the fire ladders and climb up to roofs, carrying hoses or buckets. And, afterwards, they were forced to become troops, receive military training, and become expert lanceresses who learned to stab their enemies.

Once, at a meeting for inspection of reservists, one of the commanding officers gave a long tongue to the troops of middle-aged reservists. He blamed the Japanese women for wearing their hair in foreign style—the artificial permanent waves. He criticized powder, rouge, eyebrow paint, compacts, and finger rings. Almost all the reservists gazed at the officer with a dubious look. Each said in his own heart, "We are not female soldiers. Why tell us about the women's toilette?"

Following egotistical and nasty politicians, savage militarists rose up and subjected the bureaucrats. They tyrannized all the nation. The totalitarian military aimed to put all nations under slavery. They were indiscreet, imprudent, and complacent in their exclusivism. The extortionate militarists robbed their own nation of everything, even the virtues of modesty and benevolence. And the unfilial devastators trod down their ancestors' honors and works which had entailed considerable labor. The Occupation Forces of General MacArthur were much more kind to the Tokyo citizens than were the Japanese officers. This is not flattery. I am sure that most of the Tokyo citizens would be of the same opinion. This applies not only to Tokyo but to all of Japan.

During air raids over Tokyo, at

brief intervals the hissing shower of the firing machine guns swept over our heads. And the earth-shaking thundering of the bombing made everything shudder around us. We heard here and there many people murmuring in low voices, like death cursing from yawning graves. Such murmurings were not prayers. They were not only directed against the enemy, but also against our unfaithful militarists who had plunged us into war; against the tyrannical officers; against the hideous *Kampei;* and against our governors who misgoverned.

A proverb says, "Even a man with defects has in other directions good parts to make up for them." But this time, during the terrible war, Japan exposed too many shameful defects. She behaved disgracefully in the Orient, and betrayed herself. To rescue her from the madness, the world needed rough remedies by Dr. Allied Forces.

The physicians who attended to the operation will announce to the world the clinical result. I hope eagerly that Japan's morbidly emotional, crooked mind will reform, and that she will return to submissive honesty and become an ordinary body and soul, even though it might take a very long time.

We humankind must not forget sympathy for each other—a moral ideal. We want always to have a warm heart as in the Great Love of Christianity or the *Daiji-Daihi* ("Great Mercy and Great Compassion") of Buddhism. In any country, at any time, and among any nations, cruelty is evil. Even though they make excuses for the cruel deed, cruelty is always wickedness. "Love thine enemy." What a conventional saying it has become! But how venerable and perpetual a commandment it is!

One of my treasures is a tiny, faded, pencil sketch of land and sea. On it Father wrote these thoughtful words: "The Causes of Birth and Death." I cannot guess where the view is. Is it an isle of paradise or hell, or a dreamland or a mirage? But the shape of the tiny boat is of Japan, of our Japan, of our loving but troublesome Japan. . . .